EYEWITNESS VISUAL DICTIONARIES

THE VISUAL DICTIONARY *of*
PREHISTORIC LIFE

Short, stout horn

Rows of prominent armoured scales

Scale-covered skin

Reduced forelimb

Bipedal stance

Hallux (first toe)

Foot with three weight-bearing toes

A LATE CRETACEOUS THEROPOD DINOSAUR
(Carnotaurus sastrei)
Length: 7.6 m (25 ft)

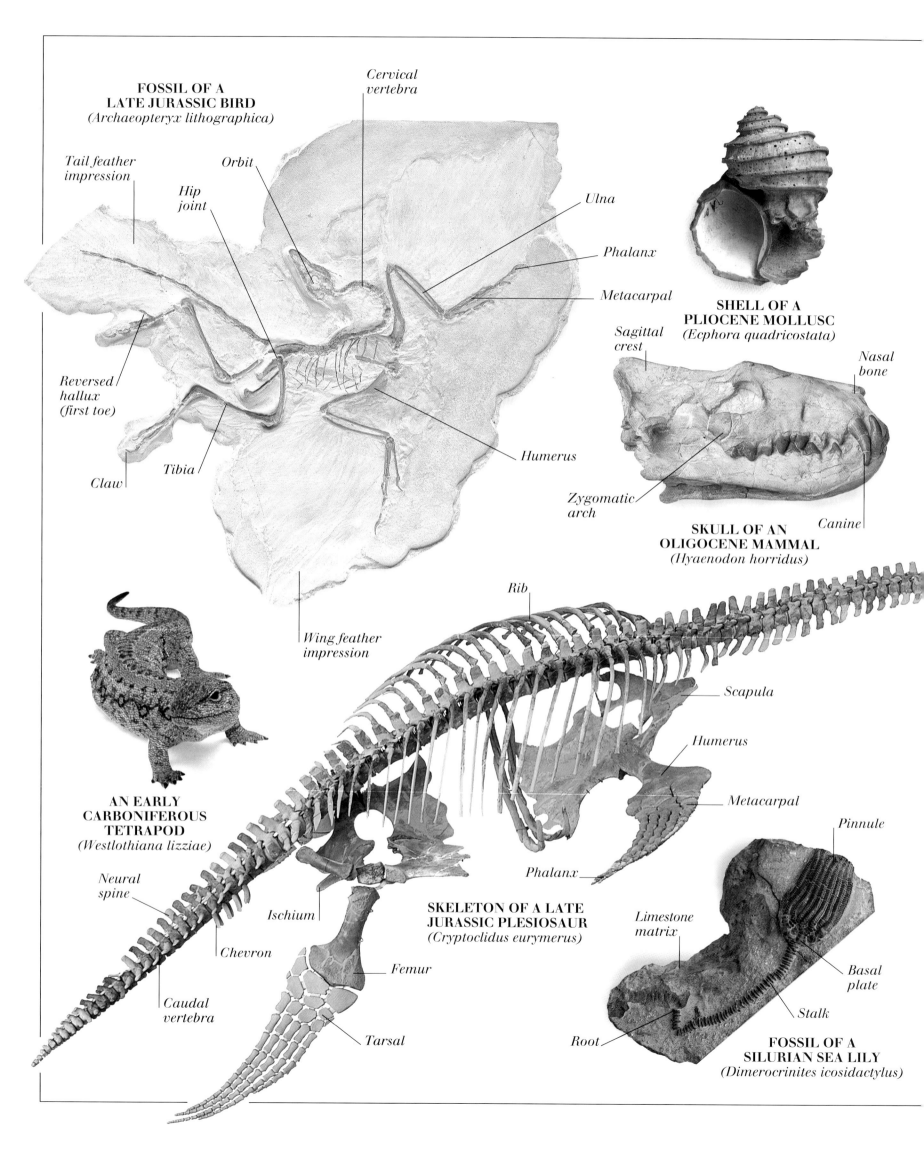

**FOSSIL OF A
LATE JURASSIC BIRD**
(Archaeopteryx lithographica)

Cervical
vertebra

Orbit

Tail feather
impression

Hip
joint

Ulna

Phalanx

Metacarpal

Reversed
hallux
(first toe)

Claw

Tibia

Humerus

Wing feather
impression

**SHELL OF A
PLIOCENE MOLLUSC**
(Ecphora quadricostata)

Sagittal
crest

Nasal
bone

Zygomatic
arch

Canine

**SKULL OF AN
OLIGOCENE MAMMAL**
(Hyaenodon horridus)

Rib

Scapula

Humerus

Metacarpal

**AN EARLY
CARBONIFEROUS
TETRAPOD**
(Westlothiana lizziae)

Neural
spine

Phalanx

Ischium

**SKELETON OF A LATE
JURASSIC PLESIOSAUR**
(Cryptoclidus eurymerus)

Chevron

Femur

Pinnule

Limestone
matrix

Basal
plate

Caudal
vertebra

Tarsal

Stalk

Root

**FOSSIL OF A
SILURIAN SEA LILY**
(Dimerocrinites icosidactylus)

EYEWITNESS VISUAL DICTIONARIES

THE VISUAL
DICTIONARY *of*
PREHISTORIC
LIFE

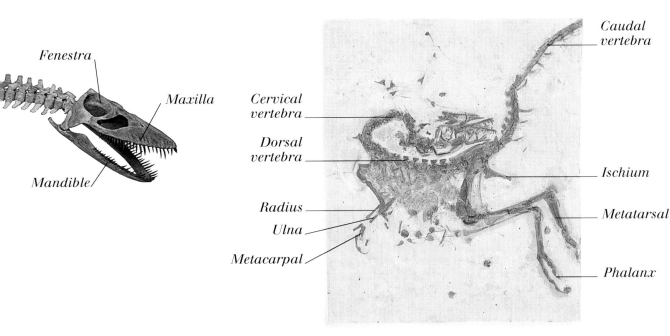

Fenestra

Maxilla

Mandible

Cervical
vertebra

Dorsal
vertebra

Radius

Ulna

Metacarpal

Caudal
vertebra

Ischium

Metatarsal

Phalanx

**SKELETON OF A LATE JURASSIC
THEROPOD DINOSAUR**
(Compsognathus longipes)

DORLING KINDERSLEY
LONDON • NEW YORK • STUTTGART

A DORLING KINDERSLEY BOOK

ART EDITOR JOHNNY PAU
PROJECT EDITOR EDWARD BUNTING
EDITORIAL ASSISTANT WILL HODGKINSON

CONSULTANT EDITOR DAVID LAMBERT
BOTANICAL CONSULTANT BARRY THOMAS

MANAGING ART EDITOR PHILIP GILDERDALE
MANAGING EDITOR RUTH MIDGLEY

ILLUSTRATIONS JOHN TEMPERTON, CORAL MULA, DEBORAH MAIZELS, COLIN ROSE
PICTURE RESEARCH SHARON SOUTHREN
PRODUCTION HILARY STEPHENS

**MIDDLE CAMBRIAN
TRILOBITE**
(Xystridura saint-smithii)

FIRST PUBLISHED IN GREAT BRITAIN IN 1995
BY DORLING KINDERSLEY LIMITED,
9 HENRIETTA STREET, LONDON WC2E 8PS

A CIP CATALOGUE RECORD FOR THIS BOOK IS AVAILABLE FROM THE BRITISH LIBRARY

ISBN 0 7513 1057 3

REPRODUCED BY COLOURSCAN, SINGAPORE
PRINTED AND BOUND BY ARNOLDO MONDADORI, VERONA, ITALY

Contents

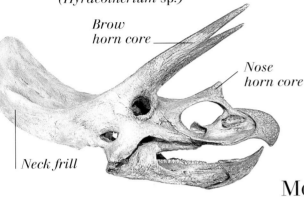

EOCENE HORSE
(Hyracotherium sp.)

Brow
horn core

Nose
horn core

Neck frill

**SKULL OF A CRETACEOUS
DINOSAUR** *(Triceratops horridus)*

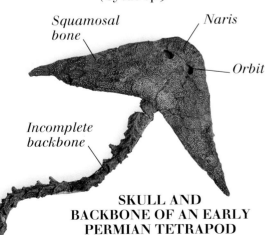

Alternate
arrangement
of leaflets

Pinna
(leaflet)

Rachis

TRIASSIC CYCAD LEAF
(Cycas sp.)

Squamosal
bone

Naris

Orbit

Incomplete
backbone

**SKULL AND
BACKBONE OF AN EARLY
PERMIAN TETRAPOD**
(Diplocaulus magnicornis)

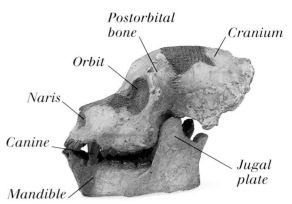

Postorbital
bone

Cranium

Orbit

Naris

Canine

Jugal
plate

Mandible

**SKULL OF AN
OLIGOCENE PRIMATE**
(Aegyptopithecus sp.)

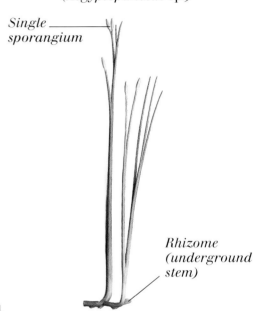

Single
sporangium

Rhizome
(underground
stem)

DEVONIAN VASCULAR PLANT
(Aglaophyton sp.)

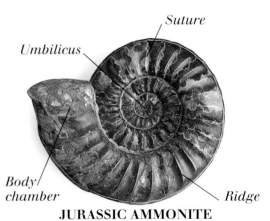

Suture

Umbilicus

Body
chamber

Ridge

JURASSIC AMMONITE
(Asteroceras obtusum)

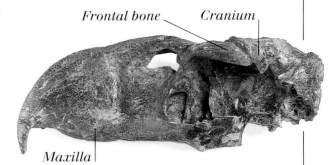

Frontal bone

Cranium

Maxilla

SKULL OF A MIOCENE BIRD
(Phorusracus inflatus)

Prehistoric time

UNCLASSIFIED LATE
PROTEROZOIC FOSSIL
(Mawsonites spriggi)

THE PASSAGE OF GEOLOGICAL TIME is marked by the slow formation of sedimentary rocks. These are made over millions of years by the gradual laying down of particles such as dust or sand. The earth's crust has accumulated thick layers of these rocks, with the oldest at the bottom and the newest on top. In many places, the sequence has been tilted, bent, or otherwise disrupted by geological movement, bringing old rocks to the surface, and with them fossils. The study of prehistoric life begins with the identification of rock formations and fossils, and a necessary part of this is to determine their position in the geological timescale. This timescale divides the history of the earth into three aeons. The Archaean aeon (4,600–2,500 million years ago) began with the formation of the planet and encompassed the time (as yet far from precisely known) when life began, in the form of prokaryotes (organisms without cell nuclei). The Proterozoic aeon (2,500–550 million years ago) included the time when eukaryotes (organisms with cell nuclei) appeared. It extended until the time when the Cambrian rocks were laid down. At the start of the Proterozoic, the only living things were bacteria, but by the end there were multicellular plants and animals, all of which lived in water. The Phanerozoic aeon (550 million years ago to the present) is the time during which many-celled organisms have dominated life on earth. The Phanerozoic comprises the Palaeozoic, Mesozoic, and Cenozoic eras (see pp. 10–15). The eras are divided into periods, which in turn are divided into epochs.

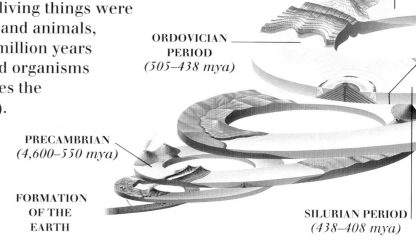

CAMBRIAN PERIOD
(550–505 mya)

ORDOVICIAN
PERIOD
(505–438 mya)

PRECAMBRIAN
(4,600–550 mya)

FORMATION
OF THE
EARTH

SILURIAN PERIOD
(438–408 mya)

THE CRETACEOUS/TERTIARY BOUNDARY
Exposed in a rock face at Gubbio, Central Italy

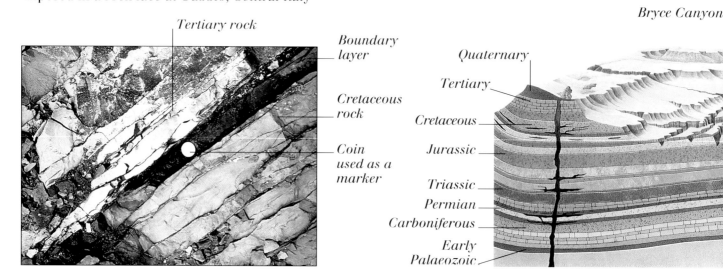

Tertiary rock

Boundary layer

Cretaceous rock

Coin used as a marker

Bryce Canyon

Zion Canyon

Quaternary

Tertiary

Cretaceous

Jurassic

Triassic

Permian

Carboniferous

Early Palaeozoic

THE GEOLOGICAL TIMESCALE
MILLIONS OF YEARS AGO (MYA)

4,600	3,500		2,900	2,500	1,600	900	550	505	438
PRECAMBRIAN TIME								CAMBRIAN	ORDOVICIAN
EARLY ARCHAEAN	MIDDLE ARCHAEAN	LATE ARCHAEAN	EARLY PROTEROZOIC	MIDDLE PROTEROZOIC	LATE PROTEROZOIC				
ARCHAEAN			PROTEROZOIC						

GEOLOGICAL PERIODS IN EARTH HISTORY

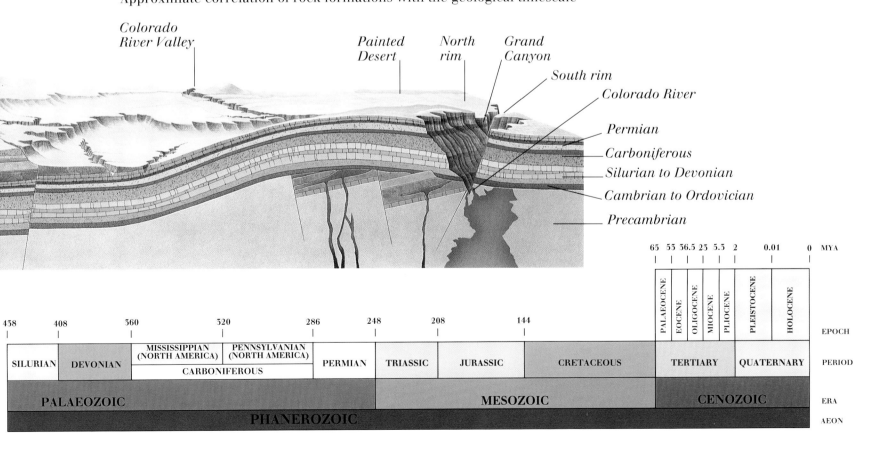

CRETACEOUS PERIOD
(144–65 mya)

JURASSIC PERIOD
(208–144 mya)

TRIASSIC PERIOD
(248–208 mya)

TERTIARY PERIOD
(65–2 mya)

PERMIAN PERIOD
(286–248 mya)

QUATERNARY PERIOD
(2 mya–present)

CARBONIFEROUS PERIOD
(360–286 mya)

DEVONIAN PERIOD
(408–360 mya)

THE GRAND CANYON REGION, UTAH TO ARIZONA, USA
Approximate correlation of rock formations with the geological timescale

*Colorado
River Valley*

*Painted
Desert*

*North
rim*

*Grand
Canyon*

South rim

Colorado River

Permian

Carboniferous

Silurian to Devonian

Cambrian to Ordovician

Precambrian

						65	53	36.5	23	5.3	2		0.01		0 MYA
						PALAEOCENE	EOCENE	OLIGOCENE	MIOCENE	PLIOCENE	PLEISTOCENE		HOLOCENE		EPOCH

438	408	560	320	286	248	208	144				
SILURIAN	DEVONIAN	MISSISSIPPIAN (NORTH AMERICA)	PENNSYLVANIAN (NORTH AMERICA)	PERMIAN	TRIASSIC	JURASSIC	CRETACEOUS	TERTIARY	QUATERNARY		PERIOD
		CARBONIFEROUS									
PALAEOZOIC					MESOZOIC			CENOZOIC			ERA
PHANEROZOIC											AEON

Precambrian time

Precambrian time

OVERVIEW OF PREHISTORIC TIME

PRECAMBRIAN TIME ACCOUNTS FOR OVER seven-eighths of the history of the earth. No sedimentary rocks from the first 800 million years have been found, all of these having apparently been lost through geological change. Sediments 3,800 million years old have been found in Greenland, and these contain chemicals that indicate the presence of life. The first living things were bacteria, which are classified as prokaryotes – organisms without a cell nucleus. It seems reasonable to place the time of their first appearance at around 3,900 million years ago, about a third of the way through the Archaean aeon (4,600–2,500 million years ago). For the rest of the Archaean, prokaryotes were the only living things. The next landmark in evolution, about 1,500 million years ago, was the arrival of eukaryotes: living things that possess a cell nucleus. This occurred roughly half way through the Proterozoic aeon (2,500–550 million years ago). The first eukaryotes were single-celled algae. These, together with protozoans (another form of single-celled eukaryote), make up the kingdom of protists. Taken altogether, the eukaryotes form an enormous superkingdom which contains four entire kingdoms of the living world – protists, plants, fungi, and animals. Multicellular algae, the first plants, appeared some 1,000 million years ago. Fossils of precambrian animals have been found in the Ediacara Hills of Australia (and elsewhere since then). It is not certain that all of these are fossils of animals; some, such as *Mawsonites* (see p. 6), are so unfamiliar that experts disagree on how to classify them.

(see p. 6)

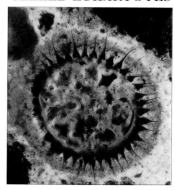

MICROGRAPHS OF SINGLE-CELLED EUKARYOTES

PROTEROZOIC PROTIST
Probably the cyst of an alga, 580 million years old

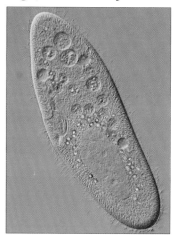

LIVING PROTIST
A complex protozoan (*Paramecium* sp.)

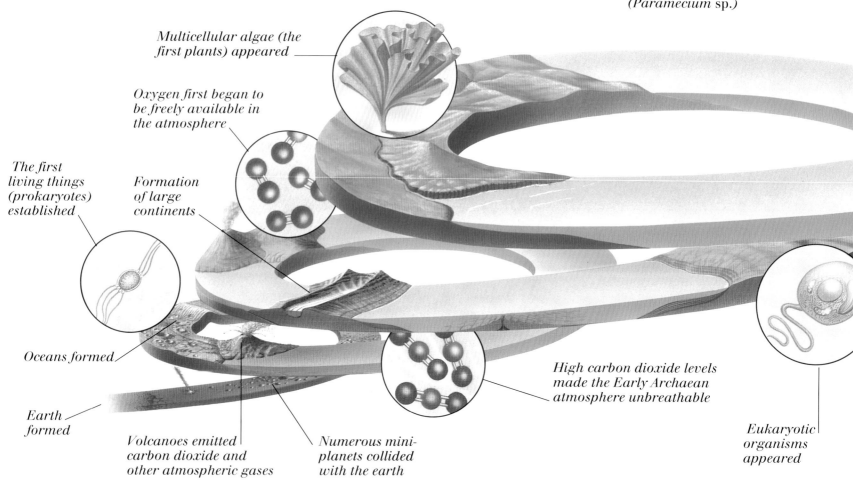

Multicellular algae (the first plants) appeared

Oxygen first began to be freely available in the atmosphere

The first living things (prokaryotes) established

Formation of large continents

Oceans formed

Earth formed

Volcanoes emitted carbon dioxide and other atmospheric gases

Numerous mini-planets collided with the earth

High carbon dioxide levels made the Early Archaean atmosphere unbreathable

Eukaryotic organisms appeared

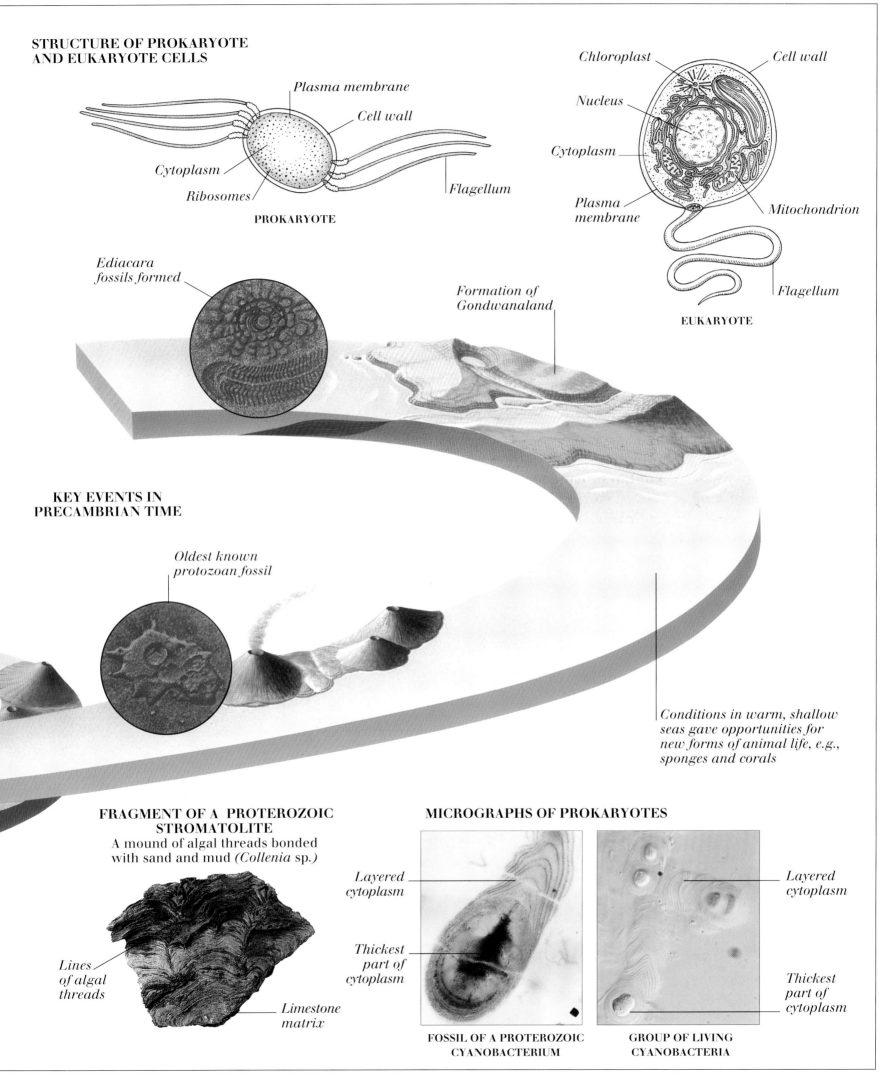

STRUCTURE OF PROKARYOTE AND EUKARYOTE CELLS

Plasma membrane

Cell wall

Cytoplasm

Ribosomes

PROKARYOTE

Flagellum

Chloroplast

Cell wall

Nucleus

Cytoplasm

Plasma membrane

Mitochondrion

Flagellum

EUKARYOTE

Ediacara fossils formed

Formation of Gondwanaland

KEY EVENTS IN PRECAMBRIAN TIME

Oldest known protozoan fossil

Conditions in warm, shallow seas gave opportunities for new forms of animal life, e.g., sponges and corals

FRAGMENT OF A PROTEROZOIC STROMATOLITE
A mound of algal threads bonded with sand and mud *(Collenia* sp.*)*

Lines of algal threads

Limestone matrix

MICROGRAPHS OF PROKARYOTES

Layered cytoplasm

Thickest part of cytoplasm

FOSSIL OF A PROTEROZOIC CYANOBACTERIUM

Layered cytoplasm

Thickest part of cytoplasm

GROUP OF LIVING CYANOBACTERIA

The Palaeozoic era

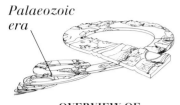

Palaeozoic era

OVERVIEW OF PREHISTORIC TIMESCALE

THE PALAEOZOIC ERA (550–248 million years ago) was the first era in which plant and animal life flourished. At the beginning of the Cambrian period (550–505 million years ago), a sudden burst of evolution took place: a wealth of sponges, worms, arthropods, and molluscs arose within a relatively short time. Around 100 million years later, towards the close of the Ordovician period (505–438 million years ago), the first undoubted vertebrates evolved – the jawless fishes. In the Silurian period (438–408 million years ago), arthropods and primitive plants colonized dry land. The first forests appeared in the Devonian (408–360 million years ago). The first tetrapods (four-legged vertebrates), arose from fleshy-finned fishes, and gave rise to amphibians. In the Carboniferous period (360–286 million years ago), the amphibians in turn gave rise to the reptiles, and the first winged insects appeared. Throughout the Palaeozoic era, the positions of the landmasses were changing, and during the Permian period (286–248 million years ago), they were brought together to form the supercontinent Pangaea. These geographical changes had profound effects on world climate, and in the Late Permian, widespread desertification across Pangaea is believed to have been the cause of the mass extinction event that brought the Palaeozoic to a close.

FOSSILS FROM THE PALAEOZOIC

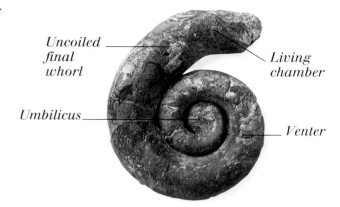

Uncoiled final whorl

Living chamber

Umbilicus

Venter

SHELL OF AN ORDOVICIAN NAUTILOID MOLLUSC (*Estonioceras* sp.)

Spore capsule

"Y" branch

Shelly mudstone

LATE SILURIAN LAND PLANT (*Cooksonia hemisphaerica*)

KEY EVENTS IN THE PALAEOZOIC ERA

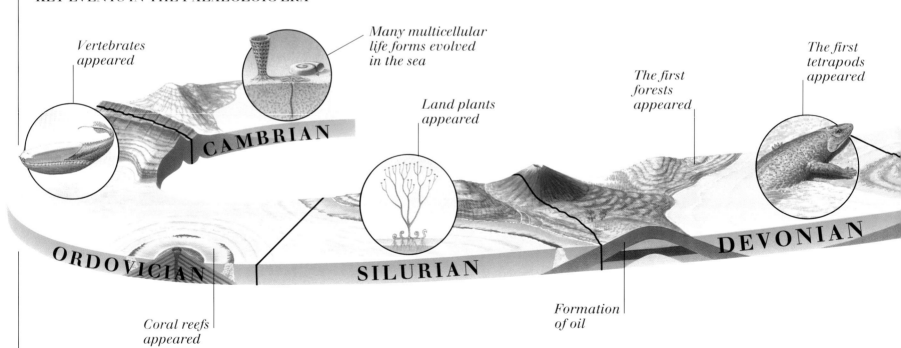

Vertebrates appeared

Many multicellular life forms evolved in the sea

Land plants appeared

The first forests appeared

The first tetrapods appeared

CAMBRIAN

ORDOVICIAN

SILURIAN

DEVONIAN

Coral reefs appeared

Formation of oil

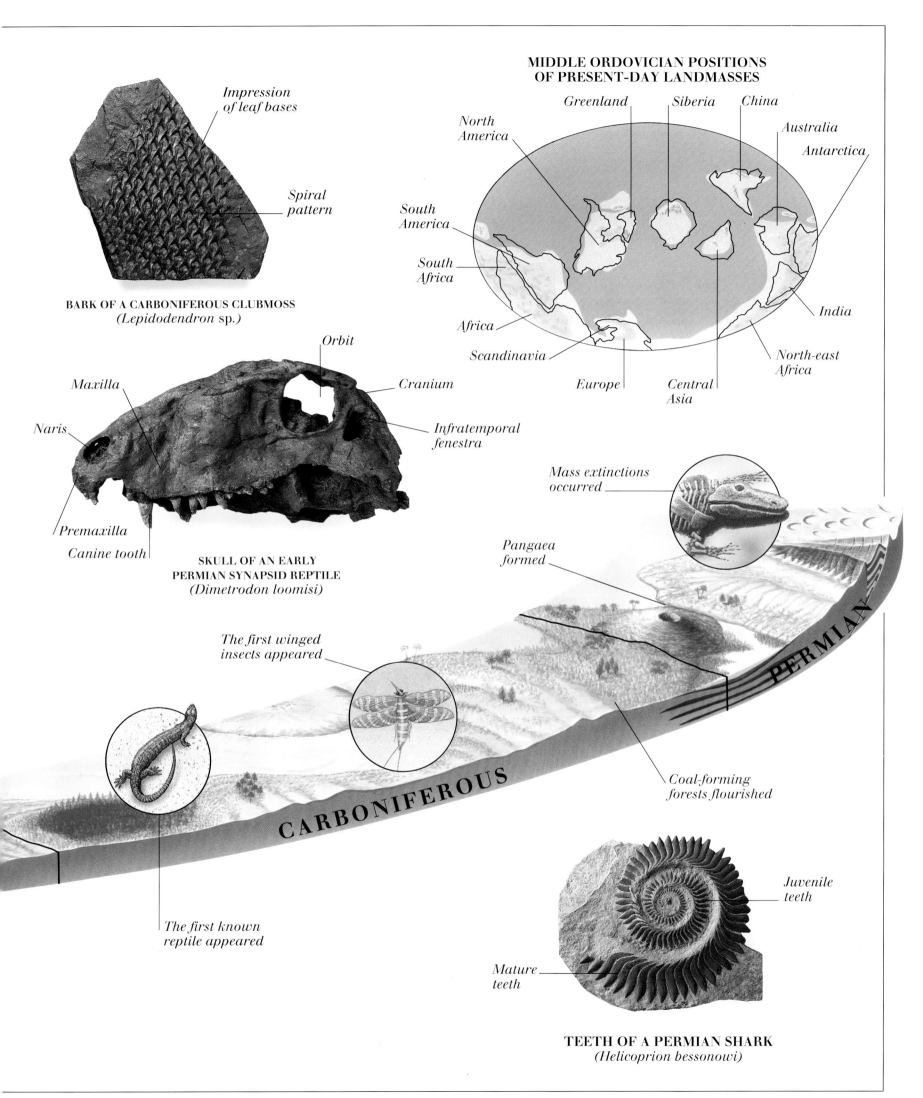

Impression of leaf bases

Spiral pattern

BARK OF A CARBONIFEROUS CLUBMOSS
(*Lepidodendron* sp.)

**MIDDLE ORDOVICIAN POSITIONS
OF PRESENT-DAY LANDMASSES**

Greenland *Siberia* *China*

North America *Australia*

Antarctica

South America

South Africa

Africa

Scandinavia *Europe* *Central Asia* *India*

North-east Africa

Orbit

Maxilla *Cranium*

Naris *Infratemporal fenestra*

Premaxilla

Canine tooth

**SKULL OF AN EARLY
PERMIAN SYNAPSID REPTILE**
(*Dimetrodon loomisi*)

Mass extinctions occurred

Pangaea formed

The first winged insects appeared

PERMIAN

CARBONIFEROUS

Coal-forming forests flourished

The first known reptile appeared

Juvenile teeth

Mature teeth

TEETH OF A PERMIAN SHARK
(*Helicoprion bessonowi*)

11

The Mesozoic era

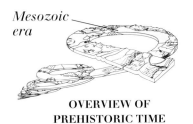

Mesozoic era

OVERVIEW OF PREHISTORIC TIME

THE MESOZOIC ERA (248–65 MILLION years ago) began with the landmasses still joined together as the supercontinent Pangaea. Warm or mild climates favoured the spread of the cold-blooded reptiles, and during the Triassic period (248–208 million years ago) a number of pioneering reptile groups evolved and became extinct. Longer-lasting groups, such as turtles, crocodilians, pterosaurs, ichthyosaurs, and dinosaurs, appeared in the Late Triassic. Mammals, too, arose in this time, but remained small for over 140 million years, their development restrained by predation and competition from reptiles. In the Jurassic period (208–144 million years ago), geological movements caused Pangaea to split up into the beginnings of today's continents. Flowering plants became widespread during the Cretaceous period (144–65 million years ago). The end of the Mesozoic era was marked by the mass extinction of dinosaurs, pterosaurs, the large sea reptiles, and many other animals. An explanation is suggested by the immense crater of an asteroid that fell in Mexico 65 million years ago. Dust from the explosion may have caused a worldwide winter, unsurvivable for almost all large animals.

Pinnate leaf

Pinna (leaflet)

Rachis (main axis of leaf)

Trunk covered by leaf scales

A MODERN CYCAD
(*Cycas revoluta*)

Dinosaurs diversified after the break-up of Pangaea

Conifers flourished

Cycads flourished

Birds appeared

CRETACEOUS

144 mya

Increase of oil and gas deposits

Flowering plants established

65 mya

Extinction of the dinosaurs

Widespread mountain building occurred

Jaw articulation

Orbit

Snout

Naris

A TRIASSIC AMPHIBIAN
(*Benthosuchus* sp.)

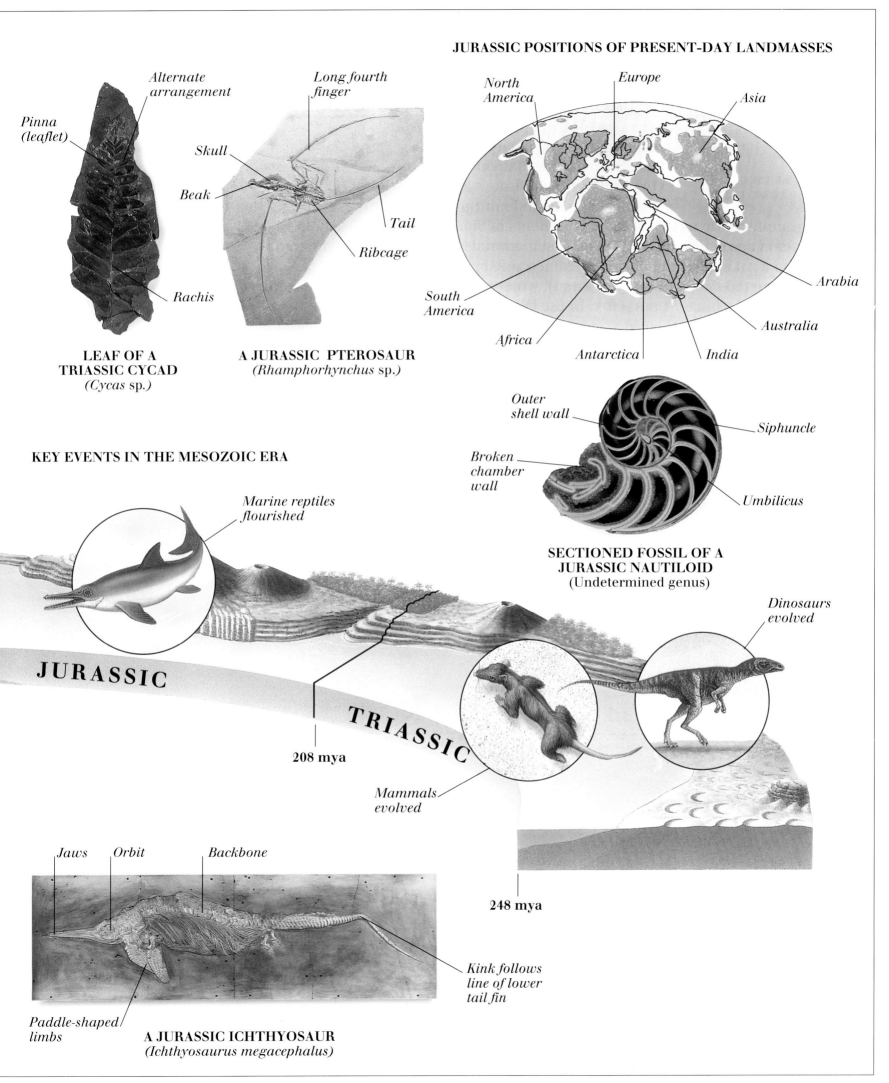

Pinna
(leaflet)

Alternate
arrangement

Rachis

LEAF OF A
TRIASSIC CYCAD
(Cycas sp.*)*

Long fourth
finger

Skull

Beak

Tail

Ribcage

A JURASSIC PTEROSAUR
(Rhamphorhynchus sp.*)*

JURASSIC POSITIONS OF PRESENT-DAY LANDMASSES

North
America

Europe

Asia

South
America

Africa

Antarctica

India

Australia

Arabia

Outer
shell wall

Siphuncle

Broken
chamber
wall

Umbilicus

SECTIONED FOSSIL OF A
JURASSIC NAUTILOID
(Undetermined genus)

KEY EVENTS IN THE MESOZOIC ERA

Marine reptiles
flourished

Dinosaurs
evolved

JURASSIC

TRIASSIC

208 mya

Mammals
evolved

248 mya

Jaws

Orbit

Backbone

Kink follows
line of lower
tail fin

Paddle-shaped
limbs

A JURASSIC ICHTHYOSAUR
(Ichthyosaurus megacephalus)

The Cenozoic era

Cenozoic era

OVERVIEW OF PREHISTORIC TIME

THE CENOZOIC ERA COVERS THE LAST 65 million years, and consists of two periods, the Tertiary (65–2 million years ago), and the Quaternary (2 million years ago–present), both of which are subdivided into epochs. Following the extinction of the dinosaurs and the large sea reptiles, mammals spread and multiplied in their place, among them groups unique to the newly isolated continents of South America (an island from 73–3 million years ago), and Australia. The first mammals were very small, and none larger than a rat appeared before the Palaeocene epoch (65–53 million years ago). In the Eocene (53–36.5 million years ago), whales and horses evolved, although the first horse was no bigger than a fox. In the Oligocene (36.5–23 million years ago), grasslands appeared, presenting new opportunities for grazing mammals and their predators. Grasslands continued their advance through the Miocene (23–5.3 million years ago) and the Pliocene (5.3–2 million years ago). The first epoch of the Quaternary period was the Pleistocene (2 million–10,000 years ago), in which a series of icy phases gripped the Northern Hemisphere. The Holocene, the epoch in which we now live, is no more than a temporary warm spell preceding the next icy phase.

SHELL OF A PLIOCENE MOLLUSC
(Ecphora quadricostata)

Horses appeared (e.g., Hyracotherium)

Himalayas began to form

Whales appeared (e.g., Basilosaurus)

65 | PALAEOCENE

53 | EOCENE

TERTIARY

36.5 | OLIGOCENE

23

Brown coal fossil

Mudstone matrix

Simple venation

Toothed leaf margins

LEAVES OF A MIOCENE BIRCH
(Betula sp.)

Cranium

Postorbital bone

Squamosal bone

Orbit

Naris

Maxilla

Canine

Coronoid process

Jugal plate

Mandible

SKULL OF AN OLIGOCENE PRIMATE
(Aegyptopithecus sp.)

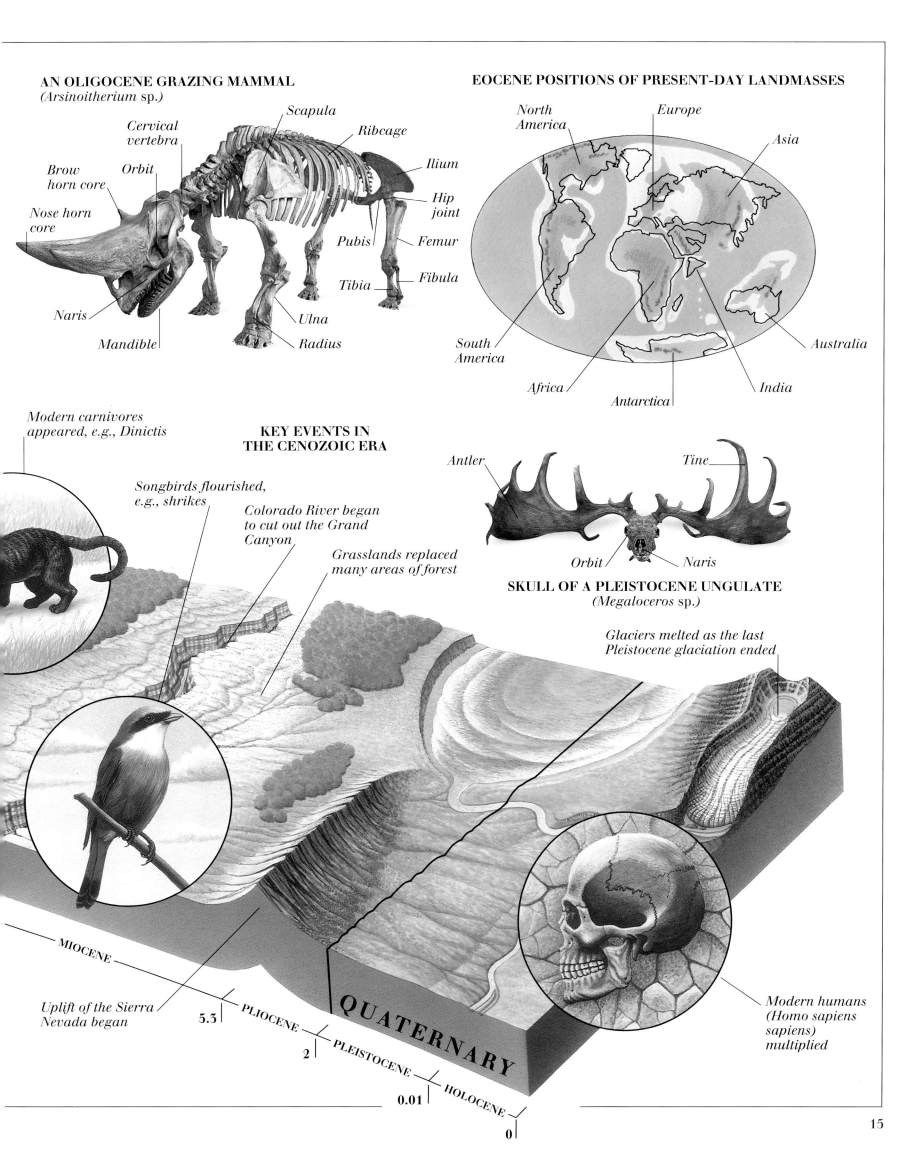

AN OLIGOCENE GRAZING MAMMAL
(Arsinoitherium sp.)

Scapula

Ribcage

Cervical vertebra

Ilium

Brow horn core

Orbit

Hip joint

Nose horn core

Pubis

Femur

Naris

Tibia

Fibula

Mandible

Ulna

Radius

EOCENE POSITIONS OF PRESENT-DAY LANDMASSES

North America

Europe

Asia

South America

Australia

Africa

Antarctica

India

KEY EVENTS IN THE CENOZOIC ERA

Modern carnivores appeared, e.g., Dinictis

Songbirds flourished, e.g., shrikes

Colorado River began to cut out the Grand Canyon

Grasslands replaced many areas of forest

Antler

Tine

Orbit

Naris

SKULL OF A PLEISTOCENE UNGULATE
(Megaloceros sp.)

Glaciers melted as the last Pleistocene glaciation ended

Modern humans (Homo sapiens sapiens) multiplied

MIOCENE

Uplift of the Sierra Nevada began

5.3

PLIOCENE

2

PLEISTOCENE

QUATERNARY

HOLOCENE

0.01

0

Spore-bearing plants

AGLAOPHYTON

ALGAE GAVE RISE TO THE FIRST spore plants during the Silurian period (438–408 million years ago). Most land plants other than mosses and liverworts are vascular plants: that is, they contain tubes that carry sap, and their stems contain specially tough cells that enable them to stand upright on dry land. The earliest known vascular plant is *Cooksonia* (see p. 10), from 422 million years ago. In the next 30 million years, many new forms of land plants evolved, including the Devonian *Aglaophyton*. Horsetails, ferns, and clubmosses appeared in the Devonian period (408–360 million years ago), and are known collectively as pteridophytes. The pteridophytes gradually increased in size, the largest clubmosses and horsetails growing in the coal-forming swamps of the Late Carboniferous (320–286 million years ago). All spore-bearing plants reproduce in alternate generations. Plants of one generation (sporophytes) produce spores, which grow into the gametophyte generation, in which male and female sex cells (gametes) appear. The male fertilizes the female, giving rise to a new generation of sporophytes. In heterosporous forms, such as the clubmoss *Selaginella*, the sporophyte produces spores of two types. The male spore (microspore) and the female spore (megaspore) give rise to separate gametophytes. Fertilization then leads to the growth of a new sporophyte.

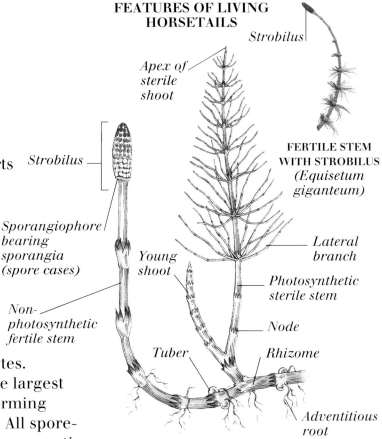

FEATURES OF LIVING HORSETAILS

Strobilus

Apex of sterile shoot

Strobilus

Sporangiophore bearing sporangia (spore cases)

Non-photosynthetic fertile stem

Young shoot

Tuber

FERTILE STEM WITH STROBILUS
(*Equisetum giganteum*)

Lateral branch

Photosynthetic sterile stem

Node

Rhizome

Adventitious root

MAIN STRUCTURES

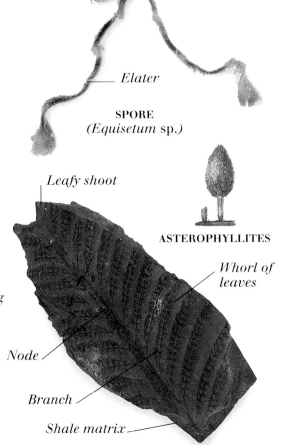

Spore

Elater

SPORE
(*Equisetum* sp.)

FOSSILS OF EARLY PLANTS

Outline of whole plant

BYTHOTREPHIS

Impression fossil

Simple branching structure

LATE SILURIAN BROWN ALGA
(*Bythotrephis gracilis*)

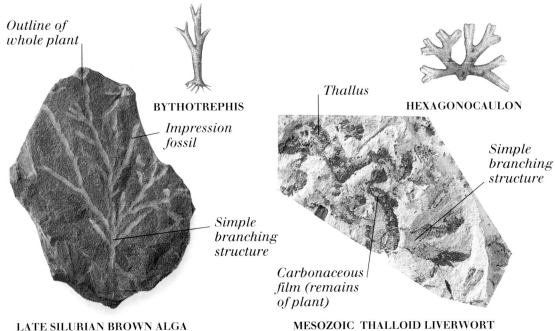

Thallus

HEXAGONOCAULON

Simple branching structure

Carbonaceous film (remains of plant)

MESOZOIC THALLOID LIVERWORT
(*Hexagonocaulon minutum*)

Leafy shoot

ASTEROPHYLLITES

Whorl of leaves

Node

Branch

Shale matrix

LATE CARBONIFEROUS GIANT HORSETAIL
(*Asterophyllites equisetiformis*)

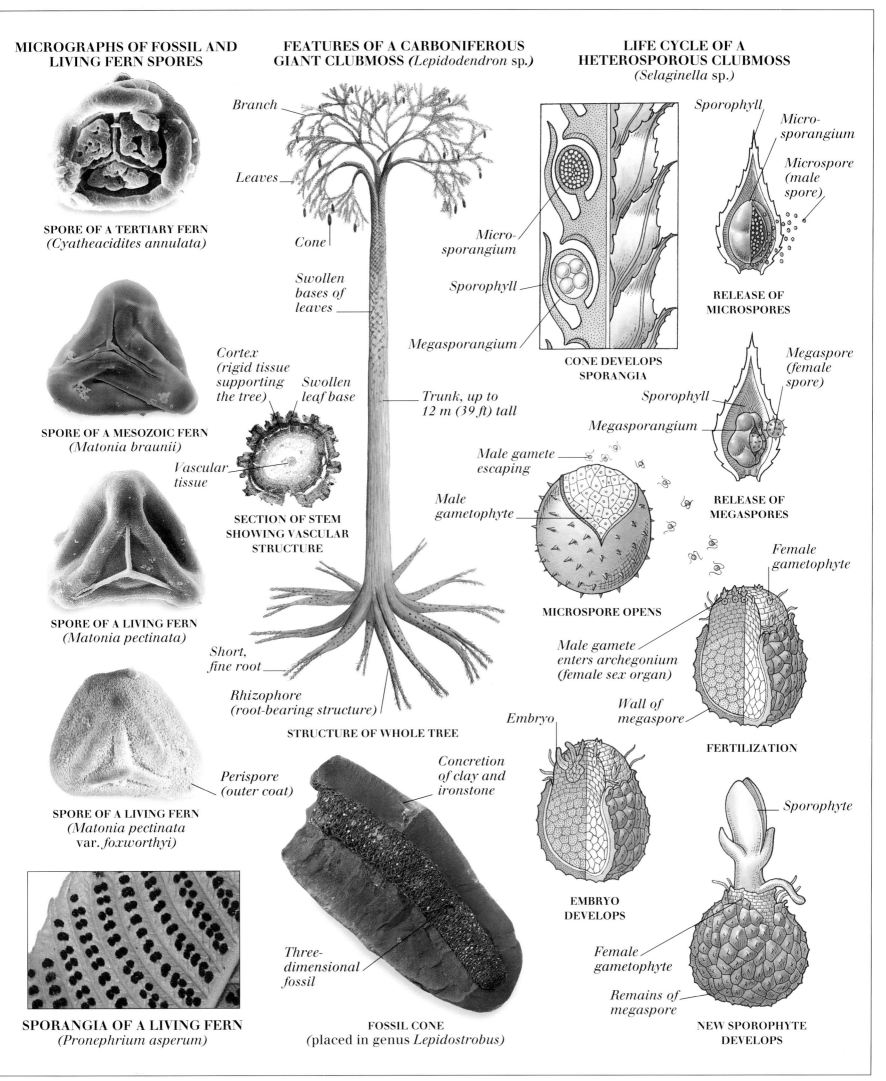

MICROGRAPHS OF FOSSIL AND LIVING FERN SPORES

SPORE OF A TERTIARY FERN
(*Cyatheacidites annulata*)

SPORE OF A MESOZOIC FERN
(*Matonia braunii*)

SPORE OF A LIVING FERN
(*Matonia pectinata*)

Perispore
(outer coat)

SPORE OF A LIVING FERN
(*Matonia pectinata*
var. *foxworthyi*)

SPORANGIA OF A LIVING FERN
(*Pronephrium asperum*)

FEATURES OF A CARBONIFEROUS
GIANT CLUBMOSS (*Lepidodendron* sp.)

Branch

Leaves

Cone

Swollen
bases of
leaves

Cortex
(rigid tissue
supporting
the tree)

Swollen
leaf base

Vascular
tissue

**SECTION OF STEM
SHOWING VASCULAR
STRUCTURE**

Trunk, up to
12 m (39 ft) tall

Short,
fine root

Rhizophore
(root-bearing structure)

STRUCTURE OF WHOLE TREE

Concretion
of clay and
ironstone

Three-
dimensional
fossil

FOSSIL CONE
(placed in genus *Lepidostrobus*)

LIFE CYCLE OF A
HETEROSPOROUS CLUBMOSS
(*Selaginella* sp.)

Micro-
sporangium

Sporophyll

Megasporangium

**CONE DEVELOPS
SPORANGIA**

Sporophyll

Micro-
sporangium

Microspore
(male
spore)

**RELEASE OF
MICROSPORES**

Megaspore
(female
spore)

Sporophyll

Megasporangium

**RELEASE OF
MEGASPORES**

Male gamete
escaping

Male
gametophyte

MICROSPORE OPENS

Female
gametophyte

Male gamete
enters archegonium
(female sex organ)

Wall of
megaspore

FERTILIZATION

Embryo

Sporophyte

**EMBRYO
DEVELOPS**

Female
gametophyte

Remains of
megaspore

**NEW SPOROPHYTE
DEVELOPS**

Gymnosperms

GYMNOSPERMS ARE PLANTS THAT BEAR SEEDS but not flowers. In a typical gymnosperm life cycle, pollen drifts in the air to the ovule, where it releases the male gamete (sperm), which fertilizes the egg. There is much variety in the way in which the male gamete reaches the egg; in cycads, a short pollen tube foreshadows the long pollen tubes of conifers and flowering plants (see p. 21). The cycad male gamete is motile (able to swim) and thus can complete its journey. The earliest gymnosperms were seed ferns, which appeared in the Devonian period (408–360 million years ago) and died out in the Mesozoic era (see pp. 12–13). Cycads arose in the Permian (286–248 million years ago), and some species survive in scattered tropical and warm-temperate regions of the world. The maidenhair trees (ginkgos) had a worldwide distribution in the Mesozoic, but the single surviving species grows (as a wild plant) only in a small part of China. Conifers have the longest fossil record of all gymnosperms, their earliest record coming from the Late Carboniferous (320–286 million years ago). The conifers began to diversify in the Permian, and continued in the Mesozoic. Even though the flowering plants forced them out of many habitats, conifers still dominate large areas of the world's vegetation today.

SEEDS OF A CARBONIFEROUS SEED FERN (Trigonocarpus adamsi)

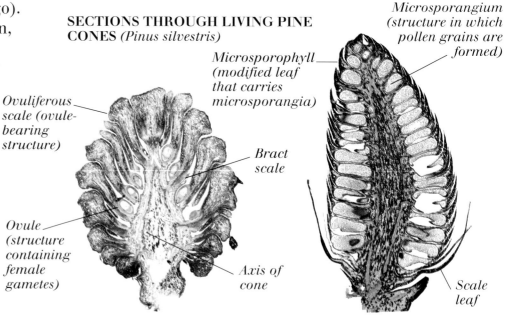

Rib on seed surface

TRIGONOCARPUS

Striated surface

SECTIONS THROUGH LIVING PINE CONES (Pinus silvestris)

Ovuliferous scale (ovule-bearing structure)

Ovule (structure containing female gametes)

Bract scale

Axis of cone

SECOND-YEAR FEMALE CONE

Microsporophyll (modified leaf that carries microsporangia)

Microsporangium (structure in which pollen grains are formed)

Scale leaf

YOUNG MALE CONE

DICROIDIUM

Mudstone matrix

Opposite pairs of leaflets

"Y"-forked leaf

FOSSIL OF A TRIASSIC SEED FERN
(Dicroidium sp.)

MICROGRAPHS OF POLLEN GRAINS OF LIVING GYMNOSPERMS

Papilla

Exine (outer coat of pollen grain)

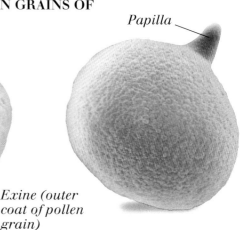

MAIDENHAIR TREE
(Ginkgo biloba)

JAPANESE CEDAR
(Cryptomeria japonica)

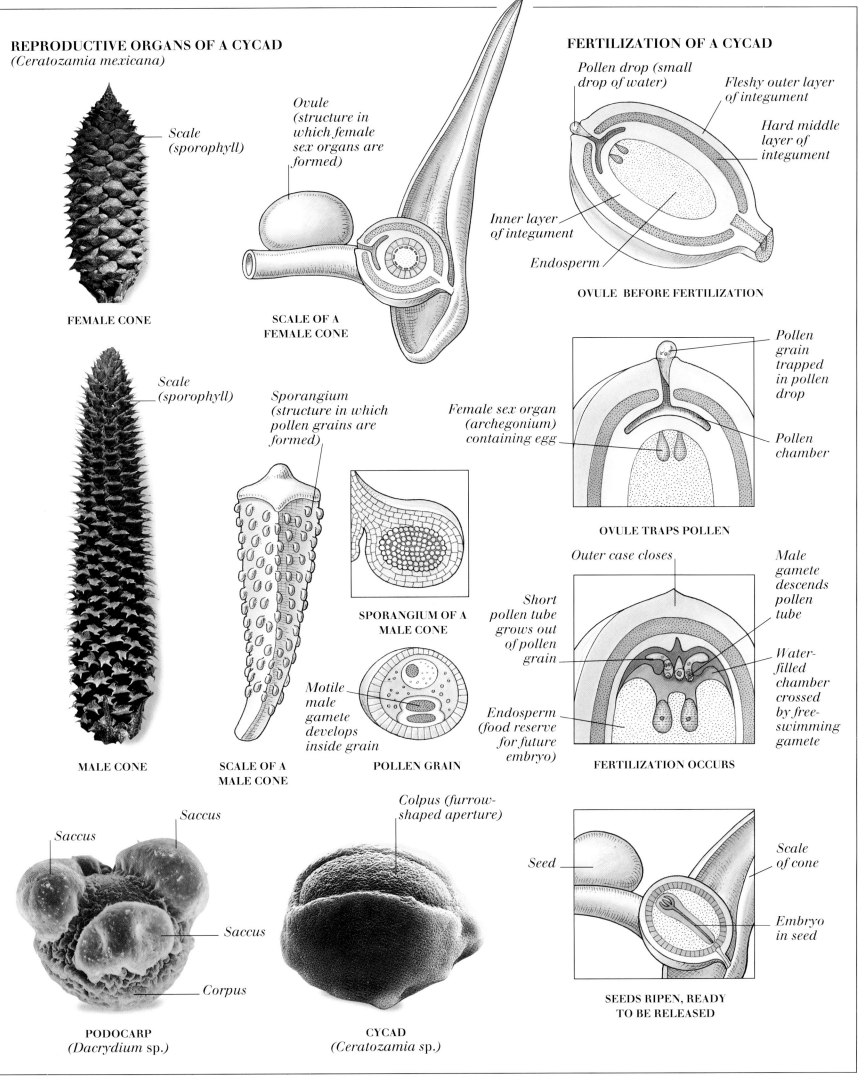

REPRODUCTIVE ORGANS OF A CYCAD
(Ceratozamia mexicana)

Scale
(sporophyll)

FEMALE CONE

Ovule
(structure in
which female
sex organs are
formed)

**SCALE OF A
FEMALE CONE**

Scale
(sporophyll)

Sporangium
(structure in which
pollen grains are
formed)

MALE CONE

**SCALE OF A
MALE CONE**

**SPORANGIUM OF A
MALE CONE**

Motile
male
gamete
develops
inside grain

POLLEN GRAIN

Saccus

Saccus

Saccus

Corpus

PODOCARP
(Dacrydium sp.)

Colpus (furrow-
shaped aperture)

CYCAD
(Ceratozamia sp.)

FERTILIZATION OF A CYCAD

Pollen drop (small
drop of water)

Fleshy outer layer
of integument

Hard middle
layer of
integument

Inner layer
of integument

Endosperm

OVULE BEFORE FERTILIZATION

Pollen
grain
trapped
in pollen
drop

Female sex organ
(archegonium)
containing egg

Pollen
chamber

OVULE TRAPS POLLEN

Outer case closes

Male
gamete
descends
pollen
tube

Short
pollen tube
grows out
of pollen
grain

Water-
filled
chamber
crossed
by free-
swimming
gamete

Endosperm
(food reserve
for future
embryo)

FERTILIZATION OCCURS

Seed

Scale
of cone

Embryo
in seed

**SEEDS RIPEN, READY
TO BE RELEASED**

Flowering plants

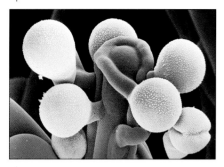

GERMINATING POLLEN
OF A POPPY

FLOWERING PLANTS (ANGIOSPERMS) diversified rapidly in the middle of the Cretaceous, some 100 million years ago, to become the dominant group in the world's flora. Flowers are difficult to define, but there are two features common to nearly all angiosperms: the ovule (seed) is enclosed within an ovary (fruit), and there is a double fertilization process. Two male gamete nuclei are brought by the pollen tube into the same ovule, one fertilizing the egg and the other the surrounding material which becomes a food supply for the seed. The earliest angiosperm families were perhaps related to modern laurels and magnolias, but with flowers that were smaller and simpler. Soon after the great diversification had begun, perhaps 95 million years ago, relatives of the modern hazels, roses, and lilies already existed. The split of the angiosperms into dicotyledons (with two seed leaves) and monocotyledons (with one) had happened during the Early Cretaceous. Dicotyledons are the larger group (with 250 living families), and include all the fossil flowers and pollen grains shown here. Monocotyledons (with 50 living families) include palms, bulb plants, and grasses. Grasses spread throughout the world in the Tertiary period (65–2 million years ago), and by the Miocene epoch (23–5.3 million years ago) grassland was one of the world's great ecosystems.

RECONSTRUCTION OF A LATE CRETACEOUS FLOWER
(Silvianthemum suecicum)

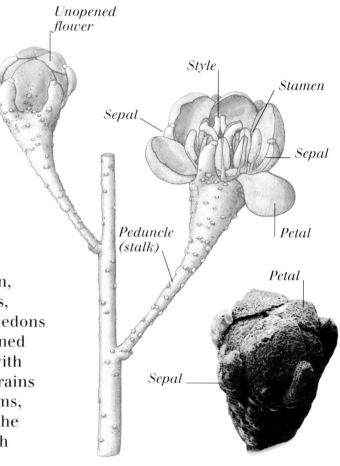

Unopened flower

Style

Stamen

Sepal

Sepal

Peduncle (stalk)

Petal

Petal

Sepal

FOSSIL OF
UNOPENED FLOWER
80 million years old

MICROGRAPHS OF FOSSIL FLOWERS FROM THE CRETACEOUS

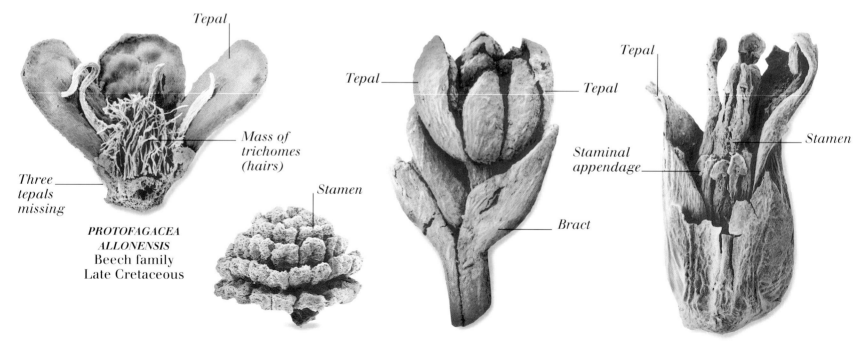

Tepal

Mass of trichomes (hairs)

Three tepals missing

Stamen

PROTOFAGACEA
ALLONENSIS
Beech family
Late Cretaceous

Tepal

Tepal

Tepal

Tepal

Staminal appendage

Stamen

Bract

PART OF AN UNIDENTIFIED FLOWER
Oldest known fossil of a floral structure
Early Cretaceous (120 million years old)

SPANOMERA MAULDINENSIS
Related to boxwood family
Middle Cretaceous

MAULDINIA MIRABILIS
Laurel family
Late Cretaceous

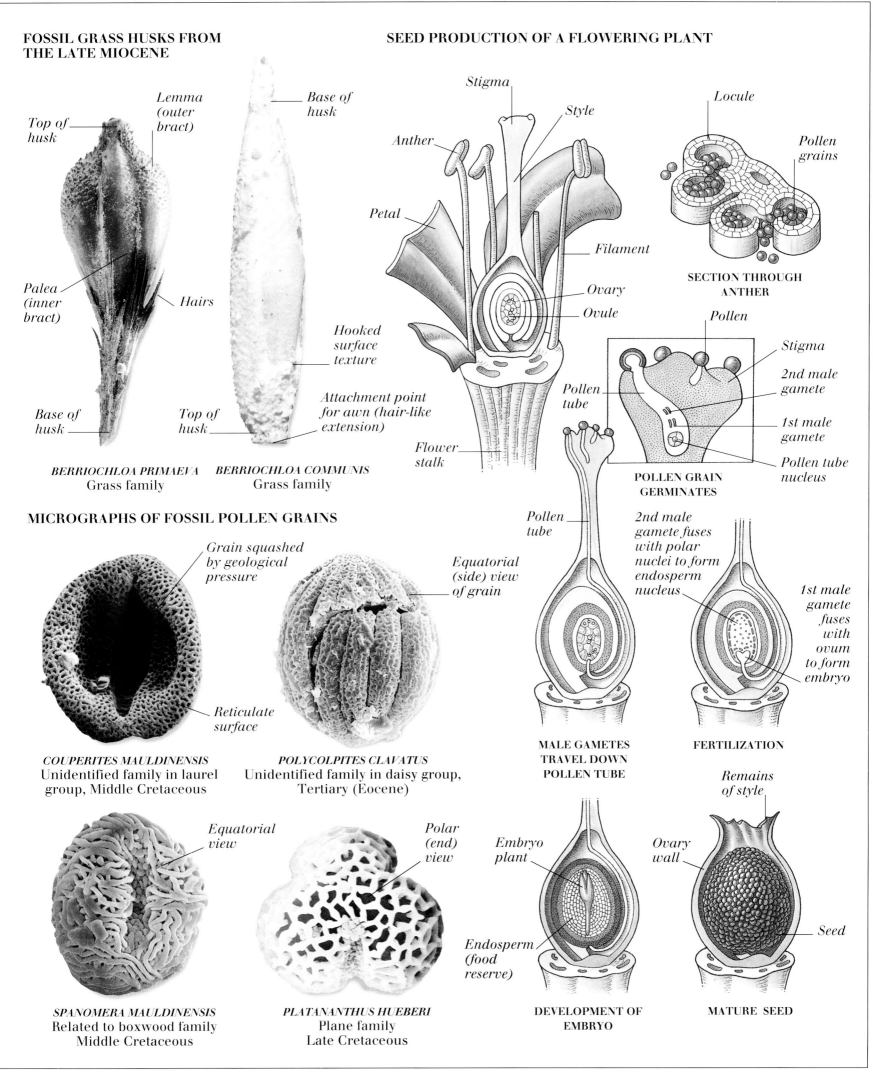

FOSSIL GRASS HUSKS FROM THE LATE MIOCENE

Top of husk

Lemma (outer bract)

Base of husk

Anther

Petal

Palea (inner bract)

Hairs

Base of husk

Top of husk

Hooked surface texture

Attachment point for awn (hair-like extension)

BERRIOCHLOA PRIMAEVA
Grass family

BERRIOCHLOA COMMUNIS
Grass family

SEED PRODUCTION OF A FLOWERING PLANT

Stigma

Style

Locule

Pollen grains

Filament

Ovary

Ovule

SECTION THROUGH ANTHER

Pollen

Stigma

2nd male gamete

1st male gamete

Pollen tube nucleus

POLLEN GRAIN GERMINATES

Flower stalk

Pollen tube

MICROGRAPHS OF FOSSIL POLLEN GRAINS

Grain squashed by geological pressure

Equatorial (side) view of grain

Reticulate surface

COUPERITES MAULDINENSIS
Unidentified family in laurel group, Middle Cretaceous

POLYCOLPITES CLAVATUS
Unidentified family in daisy group, Tertiary (Eocene)

Pollen tube

2nd male gamete fuses with polar nuclei to form endosperm nucleus

1st male gamete fuses with ovum to form embryo

MALE GAMETES TRAVEL DOWN POLLEN TUBE

FERTILIZATION

Equatorial view

Polar (end) view

SPANOMERA MAULDINENSIS
Related to boxwood family
Middle Cretaceous

PLATANANTHUS HUEBERI
Plane family
Late Cretaceous

Embryo plant

Endosperm (food reserve)

Remains of style

Ovary wall

Seed

DEVELOPMENT OF EMBRYO

MATURE SEED

21

Early invertebrates

THE GREAT EVOLUTIONARY EXPLOSION of the Cambrian period (550–505 million years ago) saw a huge diversification of invertebrates – animals without backbones. All were sea-dwelling, and most had outer skeletons to support and guard their soft, vulnerable bodies. Among them were sponges: sedentary, aquatic animals with simple, bag-like bodies made of many cells. Cnidarians, for example corals and sea anemones, were more

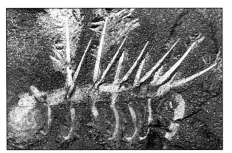

HALLUCIGENIA

advanced, with stinging tentacles to bring prey to the mouth. Graptolites were a group of worm-like colonial organisms that lived from the Cambrian to the Carboniferous (550–320 million years ago). Scientists may reclassify a related living group (the pterobranchs) as graptolites, in which case they would no longer be extinct. A graptolite colony was made of many individuals (zooids), each building a protective cup (theca). The resulting row of cups (a rhabdosome) often produced a saw-edged fossil (see p. 57). The bizarre *Hallucigenia*, a velvet worm, was one of the animals discovered in the 530-million-year-old Burgess Shale in Canada. It had seven pairs of spines and seven pairs of legs. Polychaetes, such as *Serpula* and *Rotularia*, are annelids: worms with a body made of many segments. Bryozoans are tiny animals whose colonies either lie flat or grow upwards and branch like trees.

RECONSTRUCTION OF A GRAPTOLITE COLONY

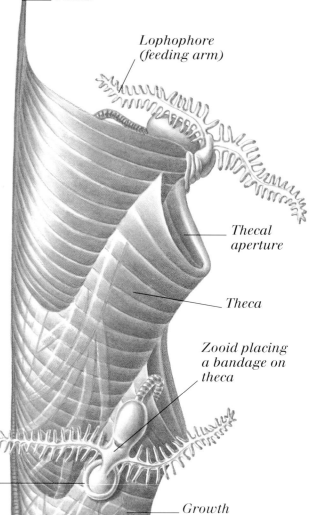

Nema

Lophophore (feeding arm)

Thecal aperture

Theca

Zooid placing a bandage on theca

Cephalic shield

Growth line

Bandage (strengthening layer)

Sicula

Virgella

EARLY GROWTH STAGE OF A GRAPTOLITE RHABDOSOME

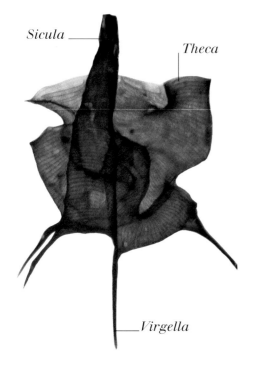

Sicula

Theca

Virgella

ORDOVICIAN GRAPTOLITE RHABDOSOME
(*Amplexograptus maxwelli*)

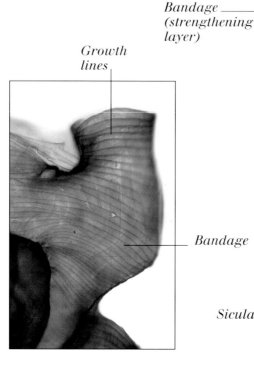

Growth lines

Bandage

ENLARGEMENT SHOWING INDIVIDUAL THECA

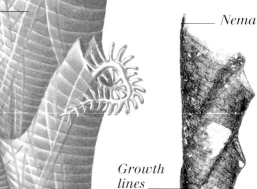
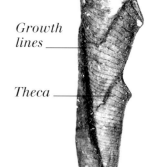

Nema

Growth lines

Theca

Virgella

FOSSIL OF A SILURIAN GRAPTOLITE RHABDOSOME
(*Monograptus* sp.)

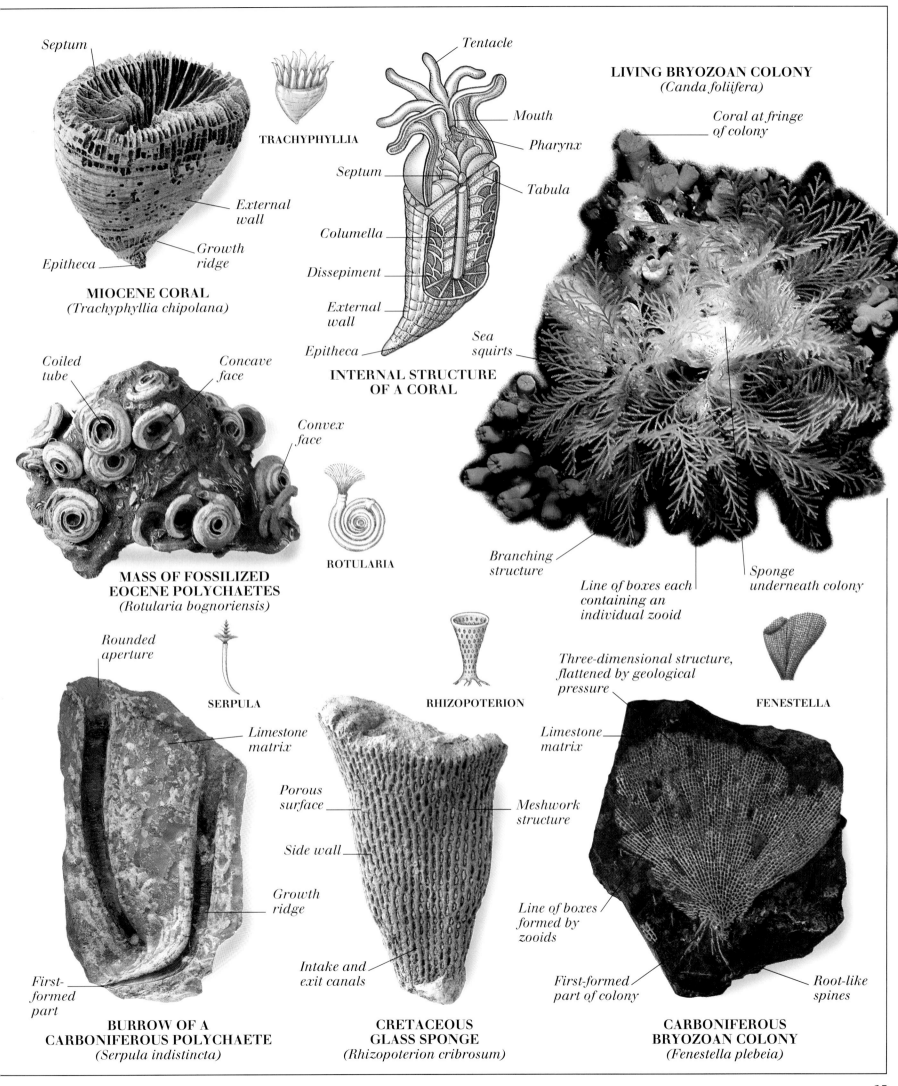

Septum

External
wall

Epitheca

Growth
ridge

MIOCENE CORAL
(Trachyphyllia chipolana)

TRACHYPHYLLIA

Tentacle

Mouth

Pharynx

Septum

Tabula

Columella

Dissepiment

External
wall

Epitheca

Sea
squirts

**INTERNAL STRUCTURE
OF A CORAL**

LIVING BRYOZOAN COLONY
(Canda foliifera)

Coral at fringe
of colony

Coiled
tube

Concave
face

Convex
face

Branching
structure

Line of boxes each
containing an
individual zooid

Sponge
underneath colony

**MASS OF FOSSILIZED
EOCENE POLYCHAETES**
(Rotularia bognoriensis)

ROTULARIA

Rounded
aperture

Limestone
matrix

SERPULA

RHIZOPOTERION

Three-dimensional structure,
flattened by geological
pressure

Limestone
matrix

FENESTELLA

Porous
surface

Meshwork
structure

Side wall

Growth
ridge

Line of boxes
formed by
zooids

First-
formed
part

Intake and
exit canals

First-formed
part of colony

Root-like
spines

**BURROW OF A
CARBONIFEROUS POLYCHAETE**
(Serpula indistincta)

**CRETACEOUS
GLASS SPONGE**
(Rhizopoterion cribrosum)

**CARBONIFEROUS
BRYOZOAN COLONY**
(Fenestella plebeia)

Molluscs and brachiopods

BELEMNOTEUTHIS

Molluscs and brachiopods are two groups of soft-bodied marine invertebrates, most of which are shelled, that appeared in Early Cambrian times (550–530 million years ago). The three most widespread mollusc groups are: bivalves, which lack a head and have a two-part, hinged shell; gastropods, such as snails, with a distinct head and a sucker-like foot; and cephalopods. Cephalopods have a large head, tentacles, and "jet propulsion" – the ability to squirt water forwards in order to swim backwards. Prehistoric cephalopods included the ammonoids, the nautiloids (see p. 13), and the squid-like belemnites, which lacked external shells but had a hard internal support called a phragmocone. A fourth group of molluscs, the chitons, consists of small, woodlouse-like seashore-dwellers with flattened shells made up of overlapping plates. Brachiopods were abundant in the Palaeozoic, but few kinds survive today. They resemble bivalve molluscs, but their paired shell valves are not identical in size or curvature. Brachiopods live on the sea-bed, to which they anchor themselves with a fleshy stalk. The stalk passes through a hole in a projection known as the umbo, located at the hinge end of the larger valve.

FEATURES OF CEPHALOPODS

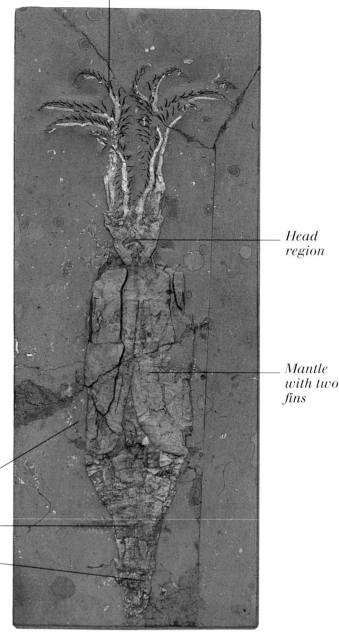

Hooked tentacle

Head region

Mantle with two fins

Shell wall

Phragmocone

Initial chamber of phragmocone

RECONSTRUCTION OF AN AMMONITE

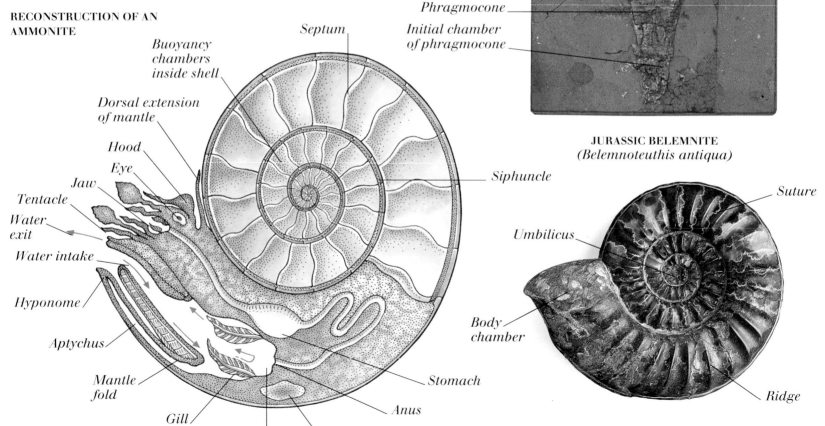

Septum

Buoyancy chambers inside shell

Dorsal extension of mantle

Hood

Eye

Jaw

Tentacle

Water exit

Water intake

Hyponome

Aptychus

Mantle fold

Gill

Branchial mantle cavity

Siphuncle

Stomach

Anus

Reproductive organ

JURASSIC BELEMNITE
(Belemnoteuthis antiqua)

Suture

Umbilicus

Body chamber

Ridge

JURASSIC AMMONITE SHELL
(Asteroceras obtusum)

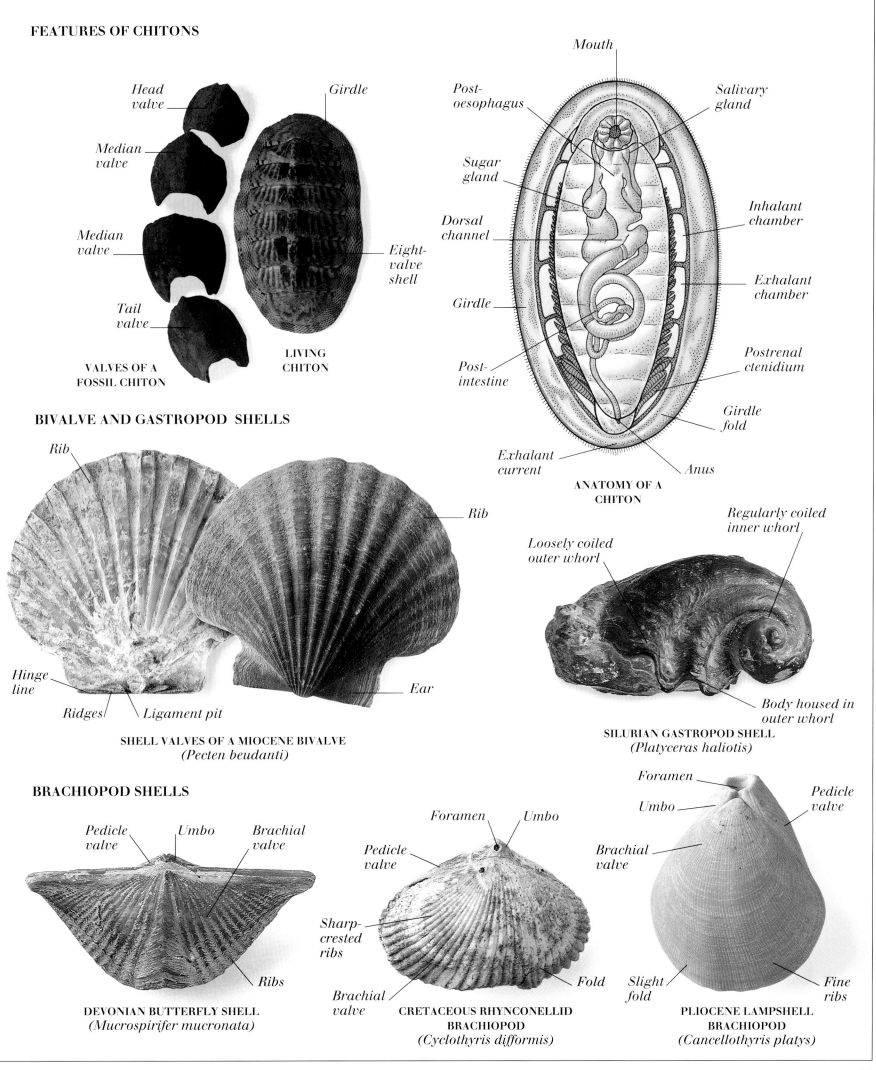

FEATURES OF CHITONS

Head
valve

Girdle

Median
valve

Median
valve

Tail
valve

Eight-
valve
shell

**VALVES OF A
FOSSIL CHITON**

**LIVING
CHITON**

Mouth

Post-
oesophagus

Salivary
gland

Sugar
gland

Dorsal
channel

Inhalant
chamber

Girdle

Exhalant
chamber

Post-
intestine

Postrenal
ctenidium

Girdle
fold

Exhalant
current

Anus

**ANATOMY OF A
CHITON**

BIVALVE AND GASTROPOD SHELLS

Rib

Rib

Hinge
line

Ear

Ridges

Ligament pit

SHELL VALVES OF A MIOCENE BIVALVE
(Pecten beudanti)

Regularly coiled
inner whorl

Loosely coiled
outer whorl

Body housed in
outer whorl

SILURIAN GASTROPOD SHELL
(Platyceras haliotis)

BRACHIOPOD SHELLS

Pedicle
valve

Umbo

Brachial
valve

Ribs

DEVONIAN BUTTERFLY SHELL
(Mucrospirifer mucronata)

Foramen

Umbo

Pedicle
valve

Sharp-
crested
ribs

Fold

Brachial
valve

**CRETACEOUS RHYNCONELLID
BRACHIOPOD**
(Cyclothyris difformis)

Foramen

Pedicle
valve

Umbo

Brachial
valve

Slight
fold

Fine
ribs

**PLIOCENE LAMPSHELL
BRACHIOPOD**
(Cancellothyris platys)

Echinoderms and arthropods

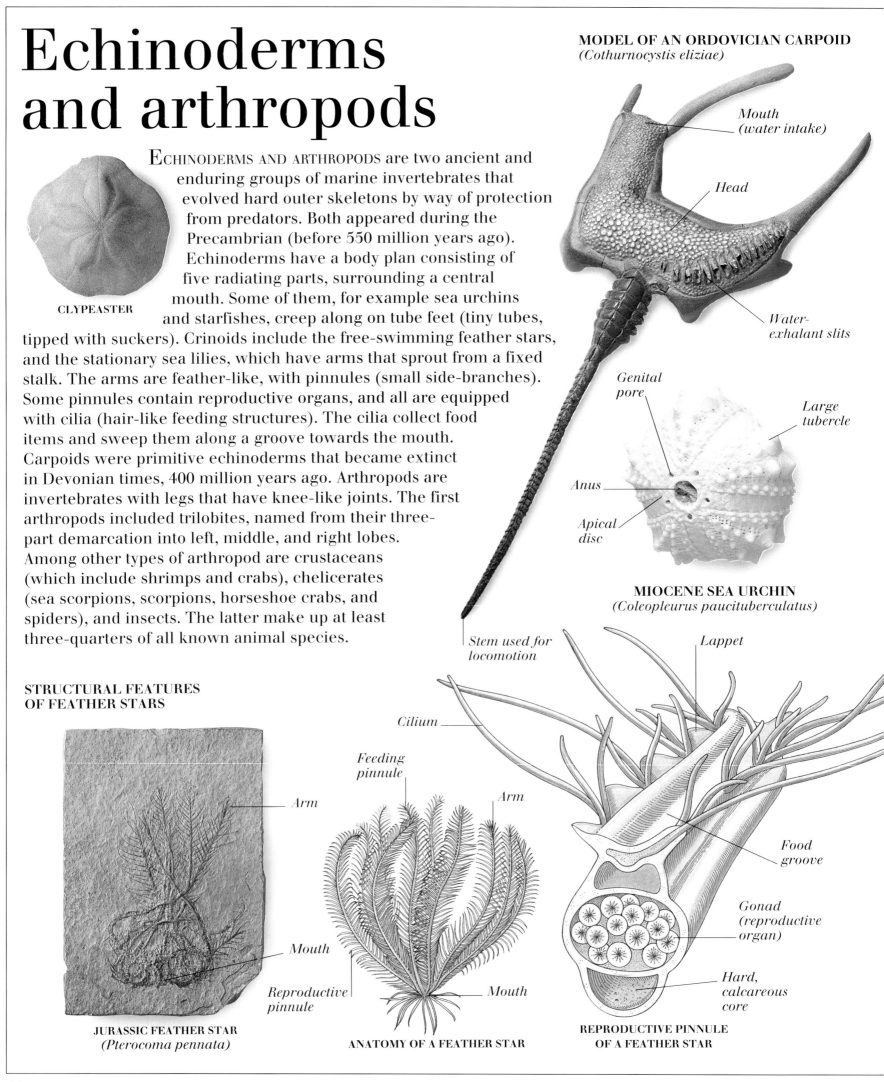

ECHINODERMS AND ARTHROPODS are two ancient and enduring groups of marine invertebrates that evolved hard outer skeletons by way of protection from predators. Both appeared during the Precambrian (before 550 million years ago). Echinoderms have a body plan consisting of five radiating parts, surrounding a central mouth. Some of them, for example sea urchins and starfishes, creep along on tube feet (tiny tubes, tipped with suckers). Crinoids include the free-swimming feather stars, and the stationary sea lilies, which have arms that sprout from a fixed stalk. The arms are feather-like, with pinnules (small side-branches). Some pinnules contain reproductive organs, and all are equipped with cilia (hair-like feeding structures). The cilia collect food items and sweep them along a groove towards the mouth. Carpoids were primitive echinoderms that became extinct in Devonian times, 400 million years ago. Arthropods are invertebrates with legs that have knee-like joints. The first arthropods included trilobites, named from their three-part demarcation into left, middle, and right lobes. Among other types of arthropod are crustaceans (which include shrimps and crabs), chelicerates (sea scorpions, scorpions, horseshoe crabs, and spiders), and insects. The latter make up at least three-quarters of all known animal species.

CLYPEASTER

MODEL OF AN ORDOVICIAN CARPOID
(Cothurnocystis eliziae)

Mouth
(water intake)

Head

Water-exhalant slits

Genital pore

Large tubercle

Anus

Apical disc

MIOCENE SEA URCHIN
(Coleopleurus paucituberculatus)

Stem used for locomotion

STRUCTURAL FEATURES OF FEATHER STARS

Arm

Mouth

JURASSIC FEATHER STAR
(Pterocoma pennata)

Feeding pinnule

Arm

Cilium

Mouth

Reproductive pinnule

Mouth

ANATOMY OF A FEATHER STAR

Lappet

Food groove

Gonad (reproductive organ)

Hard, calcareous core

REPRODUCTIVE PINNULE OF A FEATHER STAR

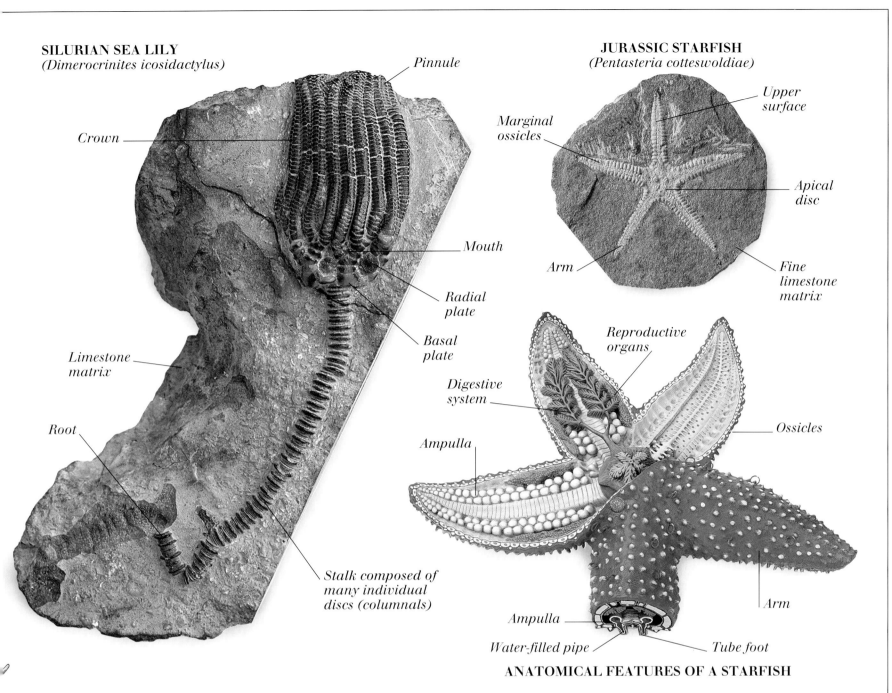

SILURIAN SEA LILY
(Dimerocrinites icosidactylus)

Pinnule

Crown

Mouth

Radial plate

Basal plate

Limestone matrix

Root

Stalk composed of many individual discs (columnals)

JURASSIC STARFISH
(Pentasteria cotteswoldiae)

Upper surface

Marginal ossicles

Apical disc

Arm

Fine limestone matrix

Reproductive organs

Digestive system

Ampulla

Ossicles

Arm

Ampulla

Water-filled pipe

Tube foot

ANATOMICAL FEATURES OF A STARFISH

EXAMPLES OF FOSSIL ARTHROPODS

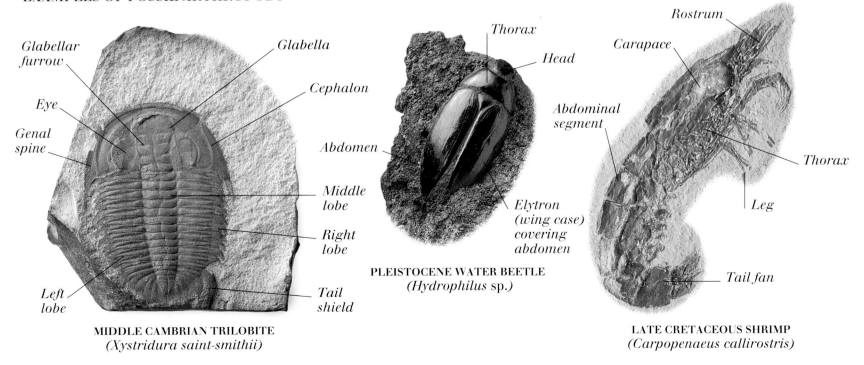

Glabellar furrow

Glabella

Eye

Cephalon

Genal spine

Abdomen

Middle lobe

Right lobe

Left lobe

Tail shield

MIDDLE CAMBRIAN TRILOBITE
(Xystridura saint-smithii)

Thorax

Head

Elytron (wing case) covering abdomen

PLEISTOCENE WATER BEETLE
(Hydrophilus sp.)

Rostrum

Carapace

Abdominal segment

Thorax

Leg

Tail fan

LATE CRETACEOUS SHRIMP
(Carpopenaeus callirostris)

Primitive fishes

LANCELET

TREMATASPIS

DIDYMASPIS

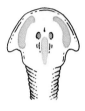

KIAERASPIS

THYESTES

THE FIRST VERTEBRATES WERE FISHES. They evolved in the Ordovician period (505–438 million years ago) from tiny marine animals called cephalochordates. These creatures still exist today and include the lancelet. The first known fishes were extremely small, lacked jaws, and had a complex brain that was protected by a skull. Their bodies were internally supported by a backbone made of bony vertebrae. Jawless fishes became extinct in the Early Carboniferous, about 340 million years ago, with the exception of a handful of species that gave rise to the modern lampreys and hagfishes. Lampreys are parasites that use their mouths to fasten onto other fishes and suck their blood. A major group among jawless fishes were the cephalaspids, the first fishes to have paired pectoral fins, an innovation that helped them keep their balance. A second class of primitive fishes, the placoderms, arose during the Devonian period. These were the first fishes with jaws (although most lacked true teeth). Placoderms had heavy bony armour that protected the head and the forepart of the body. They ranged in size from the 40 cm (16 in) long *Bothriolepis* and the 15 cm (6 in) *Pterichthyodes* to the immense *Dunkleosteus*. This 9 m (29 ft 6 in) monster had gaping jaws with jagged, tooth-like edges, and was the largest predator of the Late Devonian seas.

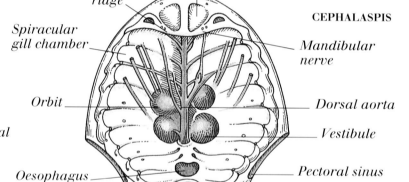

CEPHALASPIS

ANATOMY OF A CEPHALASPID

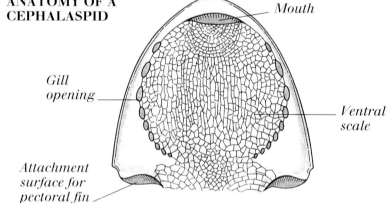

Mouth

Gill opening

Ventral scale

Attachment surface for pectoral fin

UNDERSIDE OF A HEAD SHIELD

Buccal cavity

Velar ridge

Spiracular gill chamber

Mandibular nerve

Orbit

Dorsal aorta

Vestibule

Oesophagus

Pectoral sinus

Foramen (hole) for aorta

INTERNAL HEAD STRUCTURE

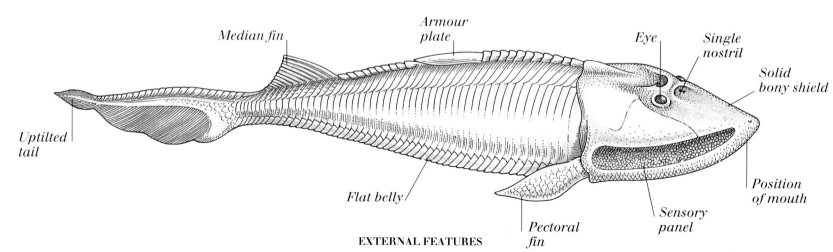

Median fin

Armour plate

Eye

Single nostril

Solid bony shield

Uptilted tail

Flat belly

Pectoral fin

Sensory panel

Position of mouth

EXTERNAL FEATURES

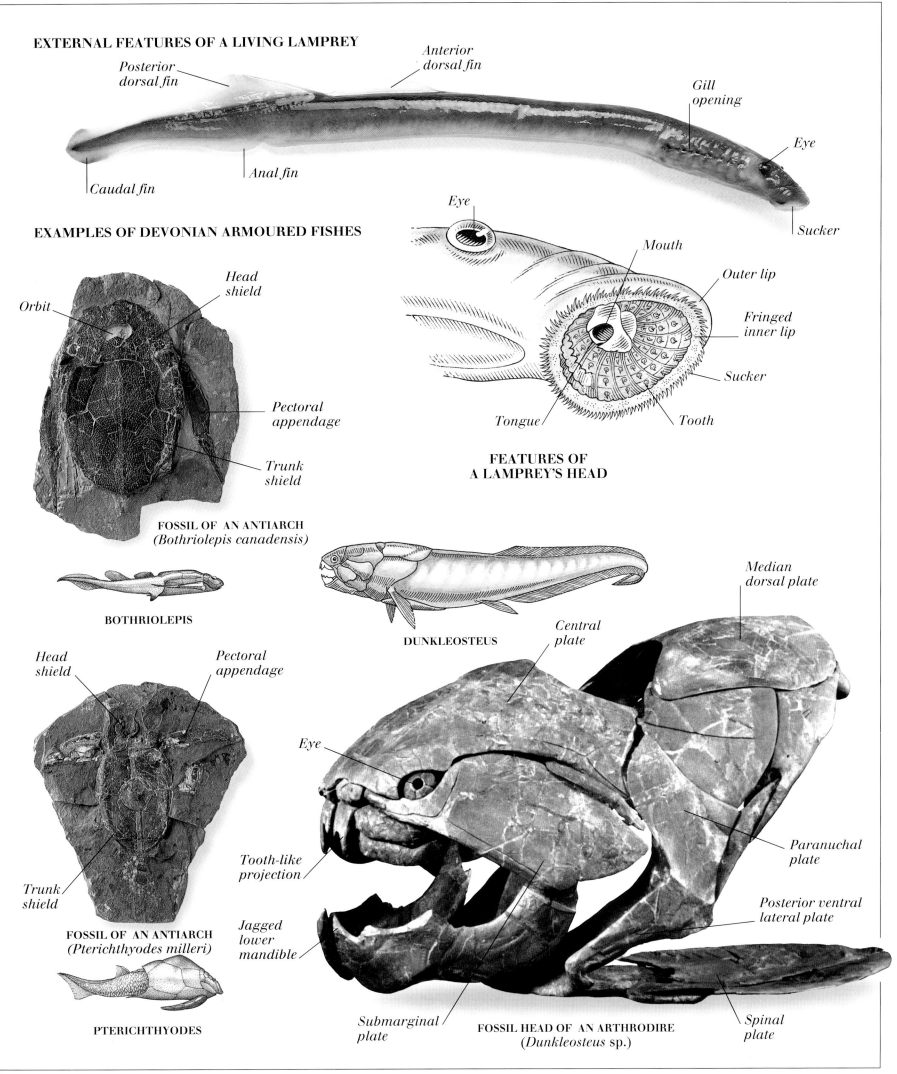

EXTERNAL FEATURES OF A LIVING LAMPREY

Posterior
dorsal fin

Anterior
dorsal fin

Gill
opening

Eye

Caudal fin

Anal fin

Sucker

EXAMPLES OF DEVONIAN ARMOURED FISHES

Eye

Mouth

Outer lip

Head
shield

Orbit

Fringed
inner lip

Sucker

Pectoral
appendage

Tongue

Tooth

Trunk
shield

**FEATURES OF
A LAMPREY'S HEAD**

FOSSIL OF AN ANTIARCH
(Bothriolepis canadensis)

Median
dorsal plate

BOTHRIOLEPIS

Central
plate

DUNKLEOSTEUS

Head
shield

Pectoral
appendage

Eye

Paranuchal
plate

Tooth-like
projection

Posterior ventral
lateral plate

Trunk
shield

FOSSIL OF AN ANTIARCH
(Pterichthyodes milleri)

Jagged
lower
mandible

PTERICHTHYODES

Submarginal
plate

FOSSIL HEAD OF AN ARTHRODIRE
(Dunkleosteus sp.)

Spinal
plate

The rise of modern fishes

WITH THE EXCEPTION OF HAGFISHES and lampreys, all living fishes fall into two classes: Chondrichthyes (cartilaginous fishes), and Osteichthyes (bony fishes). Both classes evolved from a single ancestor in Late Silurian times, some 410 million years ago. They can be distinguished from the primitive fishes (see pp. 24–25) by their jaw structure, and by the fact that their teeth are continually replaced throughout life. Cartilaginous fishes (sharks, rays, and their relatives) are characterized by gristly skeletons, small, tooth-like scales, and the absence of swim bladders. An example is the Early Eocene *Heliobatis*. Bony fishes, which include most living fishes, have bony skeletons, small, overlapping scales, and a gas-filled swim bladder, used to control buoyancy. They are divided into two subclasses: fleshy-finned and ray-finned. Fleshy-finned (also called lobe-finned) fishes have muscular lobes supporting the pectoral and pelvic fins, and some kinds, including the Late Devonian *Panderichthys* and *Eusthenopteron*, are believed to have used these to push their way through shallow waters. Ray-finned fishes, such as the Late Cretaceous *Hoplopteryx*, have fins stiffened by bony rays. The acanthodians or spiny sharks lived during the Palaeozoic and may be related to the bony fishes. Their fins were protected by sharp spines. An example is the Middle Devonian *Cheiracanthus*.

DEVONIAN SPINY SHARK
(*Cheiracanthus sp.*); length: 30 cm (12 in)

Dorsal fin

Nodule

Operculum

Scale-covered body

Orbit

Anal fin

Ventral intermediate spines

Pectoral fin

Jaw

Rounded, disc-like body

Radial cartilage

Pointed snout

Parietal bone

Pelvic fin

Pelvic clasper

Pelvic girdle

Vertebra

Pectoral fin

EARLY EOCENE STINGRAY
A cartilaginous fish (*Heliobatis radians*)
Length: 30 cm (12 in)

HELIOBATIS

Tail spine

Tail vertebra

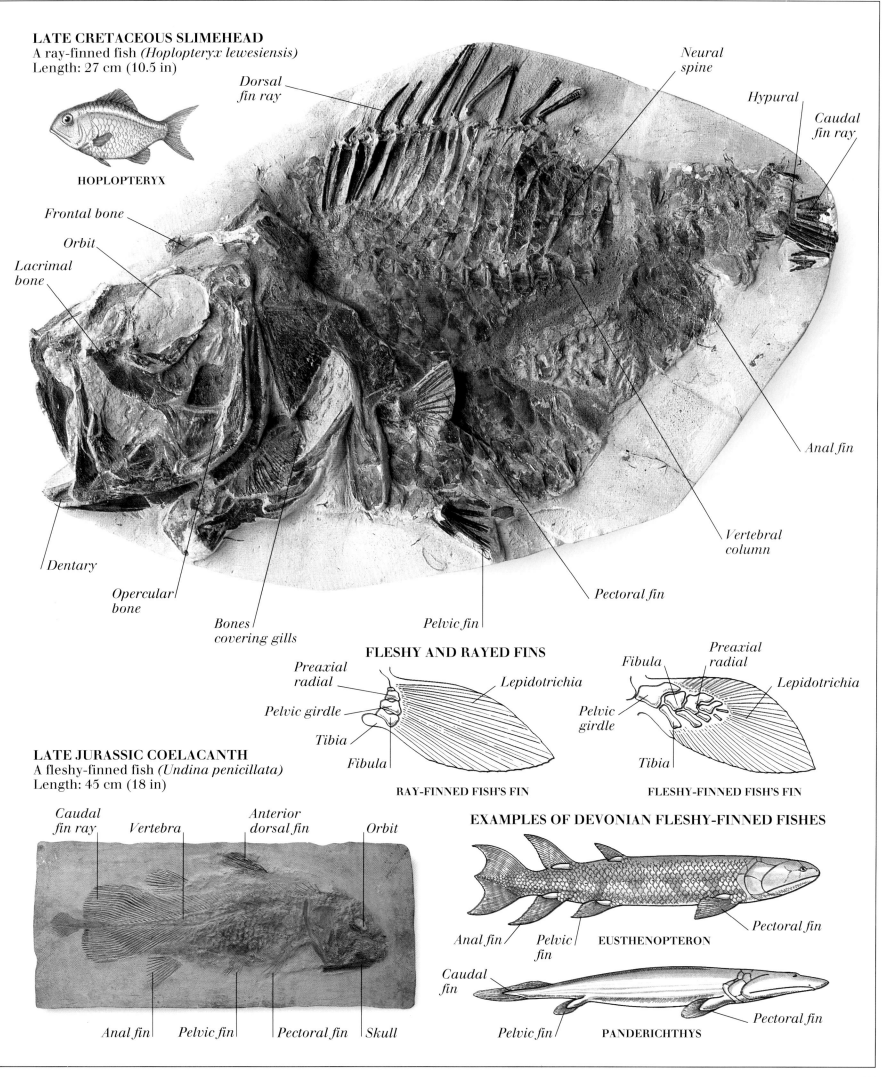

LATE CRETACEOUS SLIMEHEAD
A ray-finned fish *(Hoplopteryx lewesiensis)*
Length: 27 cm (10.5 in)

Dorsal fin ray

Neural spine

Hypural

Caudal fin ray

HOPLOPTERYX

Frontal bone

Orbit

Lacrimal bone

Anal fin

Dentary

Opercular bone

Bones covering gills

Pelvic fin

Pectoral fin

Vertebral column

FLESHY AND RAYED FINS

Preaxial radial

Lepidotrichia

Fibula

Preaxial radial

Lepidotrichia

Pelvic girdle

Pelvic girdle

Tibia

Fibula

Tibia

RAY-FINNED FISH'S FIN

FLESHY-FINNED FISH'S FIN

LATE JURASSIC COELACANTH
A fleshy-finned fish *(Undina penicillata)*
Length: 45 cm (18 in)

Caudal fin ray

Vertebra

Anterior dorsal fin

Orbit

Anal fin

Pelvic fin

Pectoral fin

Skull

EXAMPLES OF DEVONIAN FLESHY-FINNED FISHES

Anal fin

Pelvic fin

EUSTHENOPTERON

Pectoral fin

Caudal fin

Pelvic fin

PANDERICHTHYS

Pectoral fin

The rise of the amphibians

ABOUT 380 MILLION YEARS AGO in the Devonian period, fleshy-finned fishes gave rise to vertebrates with limbs and digits, the first tetrapods. Their limbs evolved from fins, and the earliest tetrapods, such as *Acanthostega*, had legs that were adapted for paddling in shallow water. Others could perhaps have pulled themselves onto gently shelving shores. Like its fleshy-finned ancestors, *Acanthostega* had a tail fin and internal gills, and could breathe air. The pattern of bones in its skull was similar to that of fleshy-finned fishes. Early tetrapods had six or more digits on each hand or foot. By 330 million years ago, descendants of the early tetrapods had diversified into the amphibian and amniote lineages (see pp. 34–35) and also to now-extinct forms that fall into neither of these categories. *Diplocaulus*, for example, was a bizarre early tetrapod that lived in rivers and lakes and was adapted for an aquatic life: the wide extensions on its skull are thought to have been used to direct its movement through the water. The large early amphibians (called temnospondyls) were sprawling and mostly aquatic animals, but the Early Permian *Eryops* is thought to have hunted its prey on land. The temnospondyls flourished from the Permian period (286–248 million years ago) to the middle of the Cretaceous (about 100 million years ago), when they became extinct. Their relatives, the lissamphibians – frogs, toads, newts, and others – are alive today.

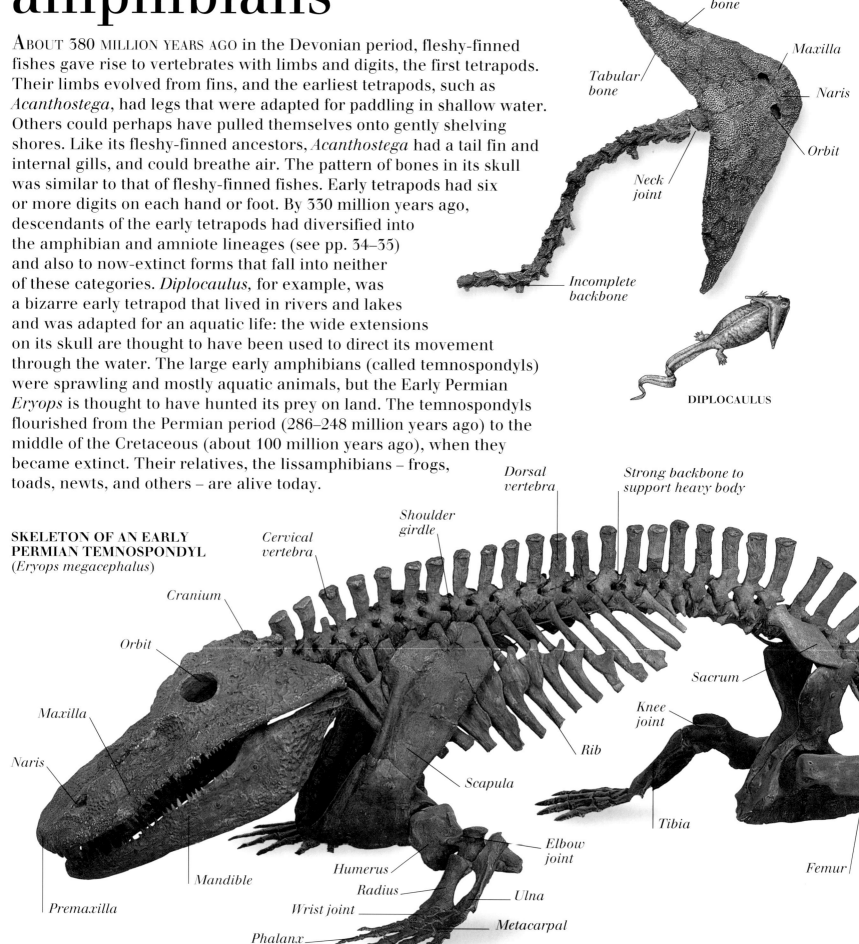

Squamosal bone

Maxilla

Tabular bone

Naris

Orbit

Neck joint

Incomplete backbone

DIPLOCAULUS

SKELETON OF AN EARLY PERMIAN TEMNOSPONDYL (*Eryops megacephalus*)

Dorsal vertebra

Strong backbone to support heavy body

Shoulder girdle

Cervical vertebra

Cranium

Orbit

Sacrum

Knee joint

Maxilla

Rib

Naris

Scapula

Tibia

Elbow joint

Humerus

Femur

Mandible

Radius

Ulna

Premaxilla

Wrist joint

Metacarpal

Phalanx

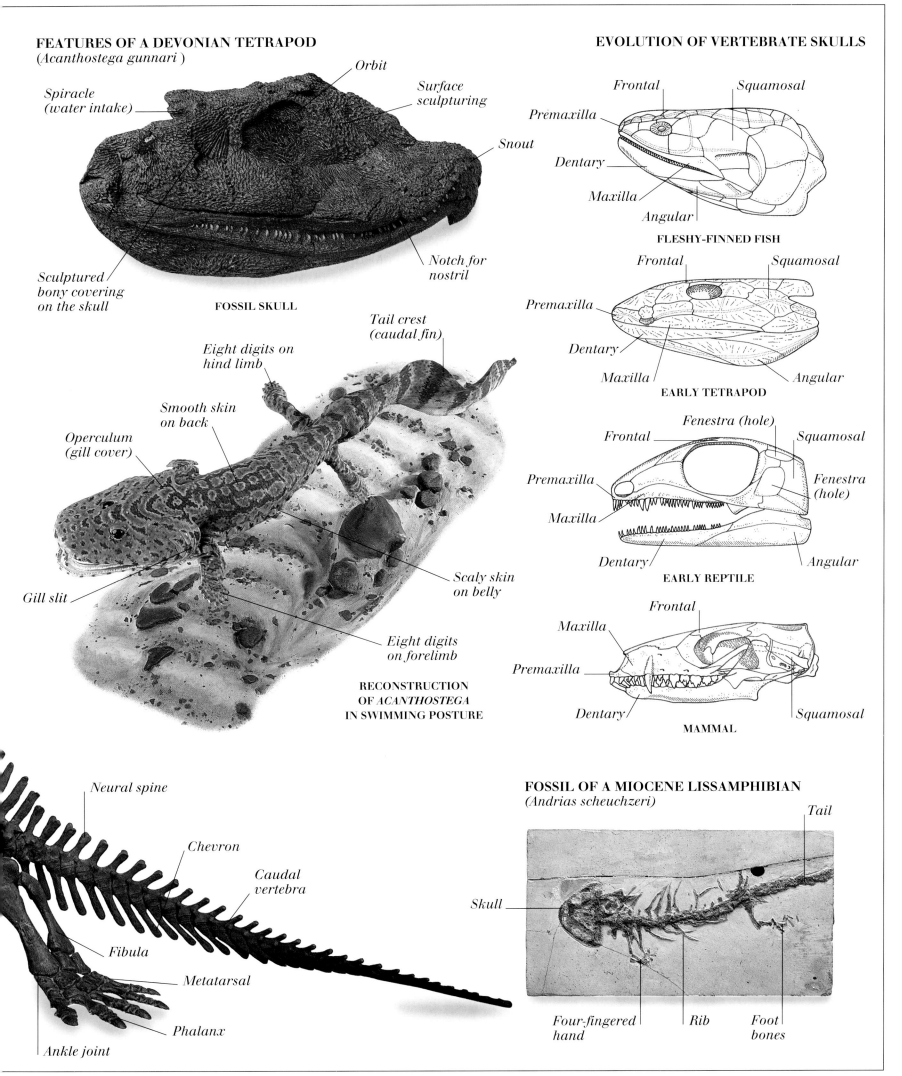

FEATURES OF A DEVONIAN TETRAPOD
(*Acanthostega gunnari*)

Orbit

Spiracle
(water intake)

Surface
sculpturing

Snout

Sculptured
bony covering
on the skull

Notch for
nostril

FOSSIL SKULL

Tail crest
(caudal fin)

Eight digits on
hind limb

Smooth skin
on back

Operculum
(gill cover)

Gill slit

Scaly skin
on belly

Eight digits
on forelimb

**RECONSTRUCTION
OF *ACANTHOSTEGA*
IN SWIMMING POSTURE**

EVOLUTION OF VERTEBRATE SKULLS

Frontal

Squamosal

Premaxilla

Dentary

Maxilla

Angular

FLESHY-FINNED FISH

Frontal

Squamosal

Premaxilla

Dentary

Maxilla

Angular

EARLY TETRAPOD

Fenestra (hole)

Frontal

Squamosal

Premaxilla

Fenestra
(hole)

Maxilla

Dentary

Angular

EARLY REPTILE

Frontal

Maxilla

Premaxilla

Dentary

Squamosal

MAMMAL

Neural spine

Chevron

Caudal
vertebra

Fibula

Metatarsal

Phalanx

Ankle joint

FOSSIL OF A MIOCENE LISSAMPHIBIAN
(*Andrias scheuchzeri*)

Tail

Skull

Four-fingered
hand

Rib

Foot
bones

Primitive and synapsid reptiles

REPTILES WERE THE FIRST AMNIOTES. This group (reptiles, birds, and mammals) consists of vertebrates that produce watertight eggs that hold the amniotic fluid which surrounds and protects the unborn young. Reptiles have been divided into three groupings according to the arrangement of openings on each side of their skulls behind the eyes. Primitive reptiles have no openings, synapsids have one, and diapsids (see pp. 36–37) have two. Primitive reptiles began as small, lizard-like insect-eaters. The Early Carboniferous animal *Westlothiana lizziae* may be the earliest known primitive reptile. Such primitive reptiles became extinct in the Late Triassic. The synapsids (also known as the mammal-like reptiles) lived from Late Carboniferous to Early Jurassic times. Early synapsids were cold-blooded creatures with a sprawling gait and posture, and included pelycosaurs. An example of these is *Edaphosaurus*, a 3 m (10 ft) long herbivore with a skin sail on its back, held up by tall spines, which were upward projections from its backbone. Therapsids were an advanced group of synapsids. Herbivores included the 3 m (10 ft) long *Sinokannemeyeria*, while carnivores included *Cynognathus*, which was 2 m (6 ft 6 in) long .

**SKELETON OF AN EARLY
TRIASSIC SYNAPSID REPTILE**
(Sinokannemeyeria yinchiaoensis)
Length: 3 m (10 ft)

Scapula

Cervical
vertebra

Infratemporal
fenestra

Cranium

Orbit

Naris

Maxilla

Dentary
bone

Mandible

Ulna

Elbow
joint

Wrist joint

Metacarpal

Phalanx

SINOKANNEMEYERIA

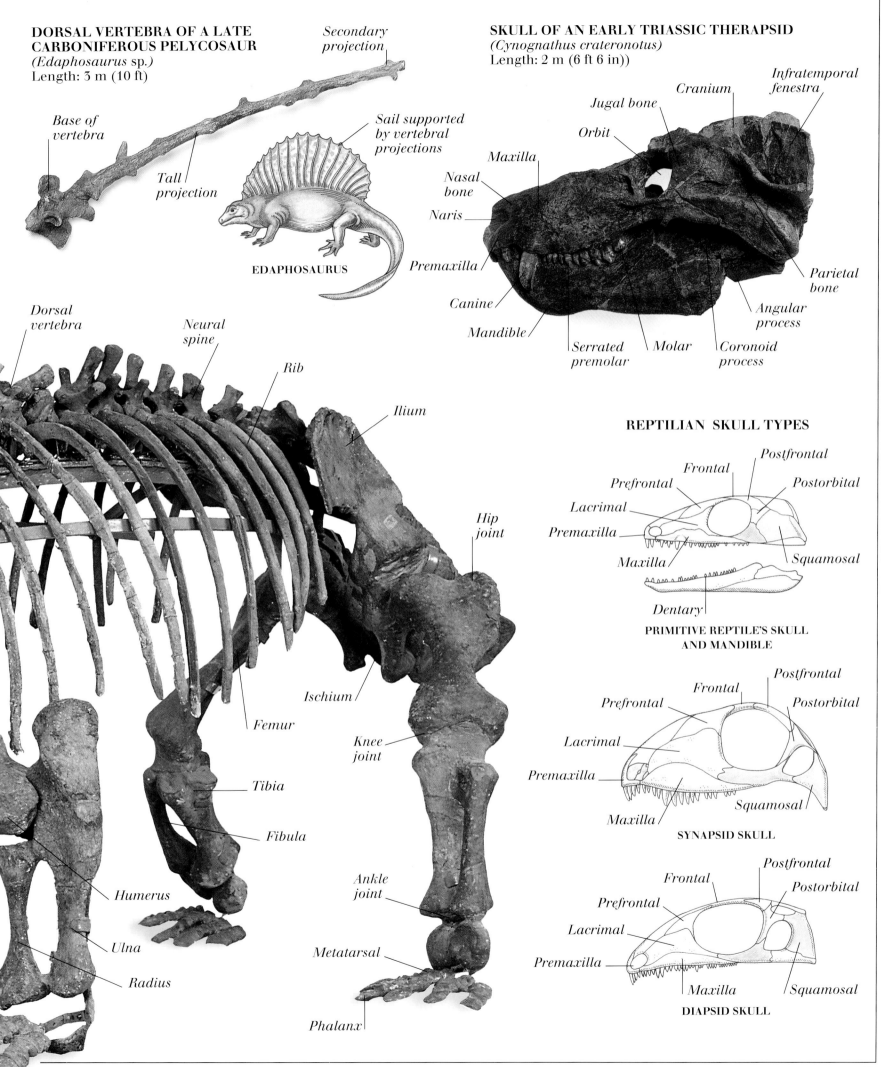

DORSAL VERTEBRA OF A LATE CARBONIFEROUS PELYCOSAUR
(Edaphosaurus sp.)
Length: 3 m (10 ft)

Secondary projection

Base of vertebra

Tall projection

Sail supported by vertebral projections

EDAPHOSAURUS

Dorsal vertebra

Neural spine

Rib

Ilium

Hip joint

Ischium

Femur

Knee joint

Tibia

Fibula

Humerus

Ulna

Radius

Ankle joint

Metatarsal

Phalanx

SKULL OF AN EARLY TRIASSIC THERAPSID
(Cynognathus crateronotus)
Length: 2 m (6 ft 6 in))

Cranium

Jugal bone

Infratemporal fenestra

Orbit

Maxilla

Nasal bone

Naris

Premaxilla

Canine

Mandible

Serrated premolar

Molar

Coronoid process

Angular process

Parietal bone

REPTILIAN SKULL TYPES

Postfrontal

Frontal

Prefrontal

Postorbital

Lacrimal

Premaxilla

Maxilla

Squamosal

Dentary

PRIMITIVE REPTILE'S SKULL AND MANDIBLE

Postfrontal

Frontal

Prefrontal

Postorbital

Lacrimal

Premaxilla

Maxilla

Squamosal

SYNAPSID SKULL

Postfrontal

Frontal

Prefrontal

Postorbital

Lacrimal

Premaxilla

Maxilla

Squamosal

DIAPSID SKULL

Marine reptiles

THE FIRST DIAPSID REPTILES evolved some 300 million years ago in the Late Carboniferous. All modern reptiles except turtles, and many extinct groups as well, evolved from these animals. Among their extinct descendants were various swimming reptiles of the Mesozoic era (248–65 million years ago). In the Triassic period (248–208 million years ago) there were two major types of sea reptiles. The slender nothosaurs swam by thrusting water backwards with their tails, and fed by spearing fish with sharp, interlocking teeth. The sturdy placodonts fed on shellfish, harvesting them with shovel-like front teeth and crushing them against specialized back teeth. By the Jurassic period (208–144 million years ago), these groups had died out, to be replaced by plesiosaurs and ichthyosaurs, whose limbs had evolved into flippers. Short-necked plesiosaurs were known as pliosaurs. The larger pliosaurs hunted ichthyosaurs – streamlined, dolphin-like reptiles, with fins, flippers, and long, narrow jaws. By the close of the Mesozoic era, the ichthyosaurs had been replaced by mosasaurs: sea lizards with paddle-shaped limbs and sharp-toothed jaws.

NINETEENTH-CENTURY RECONSTRUCTION OF A MESOZOIC SEASCAPE

Fish-like tail

Streamlined body

Fin-like flipper

TYLOSAURUS
A Late Cretaceous mosasaur
Length: 6 m (19 ft 6 in)

Rib

Dorsal vertebra

Sacral vertebra

Sacrum

SKELETON OF A LATE JURASSIC PLESIOSAUR
(*Cryptoclidus eurymerus*)
Length: 4 m (13 ft)

Neural spine

Ilium

Ischium

Chevron

Caudal vertebra

Belly rib

Humerus

Carpal

Sternum

Pelvic girdle

Phalanx

Femur

Tarsal

Phalanx

CRYPTOCLIDUS

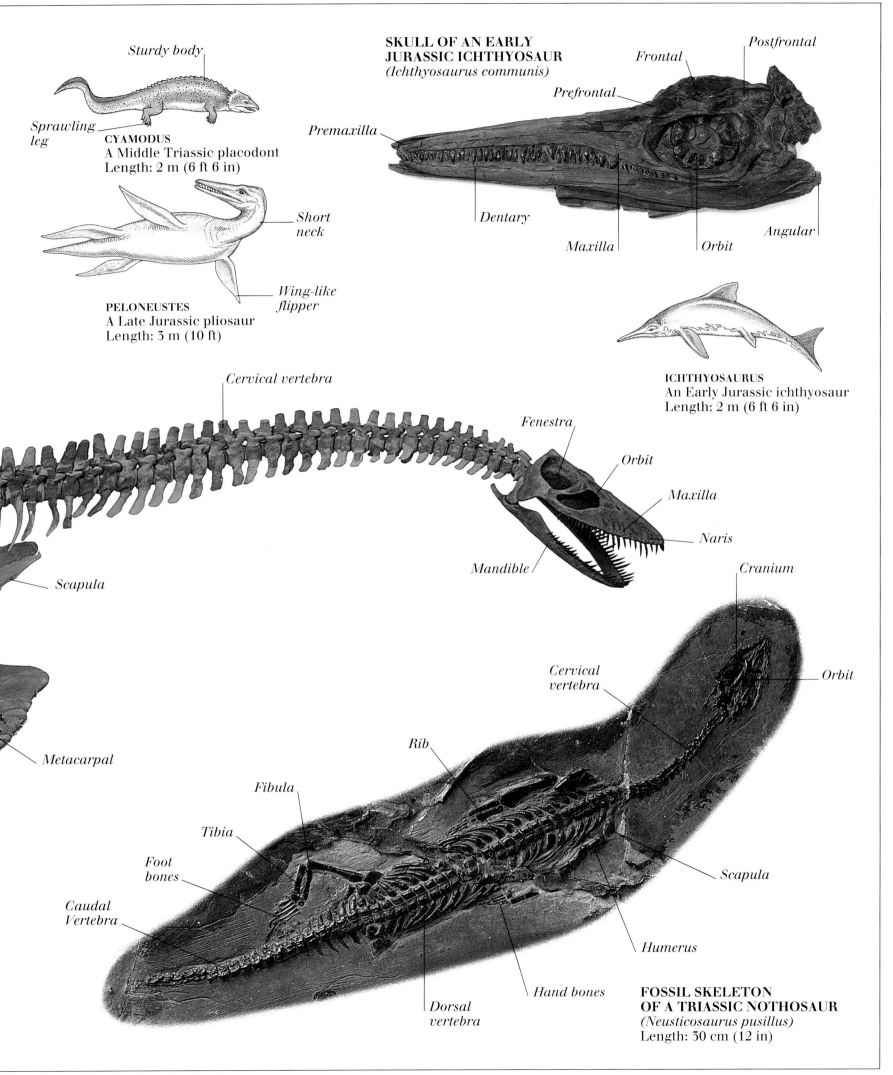

Sturdy body

Sprawling leg

CYAMODUS
A Middle Triassic placodont
Length: 2 m (6 ft 6 in)

Short neck

Wing-like flipper

PELONEUSTES
A Late Jurassic pliosaur
Length: 3 m (10 ft)

Cervical vertebra

Scapula

Metacarpal

SKULL OF AN EARLY JURASSIC ICHTHYOSAUR
(Ichthyosaurus communis)

Frontal

Postfrontal

Prefrontal

Premaxilla

Dentary

Maxilla

Orbit

Angular

ICHTHYOSAURUS
An Early Jurassic ichthyosaur
Length: 2 m (6 ft 6 in)

Fenestra

Orbit

Maxilla

Naris

Mandible

Cranium

Cervical vertebra

Orbit

Rib

Fibula

Tibia

Foot bones

Caudal Vertebra

Dorsal vertebra

Hand bones

Humerus

Scapula

FOSSIL SKELETON OF A TRIASSIC NOTHOSAUR
(Neusticosaurus pusillus)
Length: 30 cm (12 in)

Relatives of the dinosaurs

THE ARCHOSAUROMORPHS were a diapsid (see p. 34) reptile group that included rhynchosaurs and archosaurs – diapsids with an extra opening in the skull ahead of each eye. Archosaurs dominated life on land throughout much of the Mesozoic era (248–65 million years ago). In the Triassic period (248–208 million years ago), archosaurs diversified into four sub-groups: "thecodonts", dinosaurs, pterosaurs, and crocodilians. "Thecodonts", the first to evolve, are named in quotation marks because there is some doubt that they formed a closely related group. The Early Triassic thecodont *Euparkeria* was partially bipedal; it could tuck in its knees and rear up on its hind legs to run. In the Late Triassic, thecodonts gave rise to dinosaurs and pterosaurs. Pterosaurs were flying reptiles with skin-covered wings. Crocodilians included *Deinosuchus*, possibly the largest-ever crocodile, living in the Late Cretaceous (97.5–65 million years ago). All thecodonts died out by the end of the Triassic; the dinosaurs and pterosaurs lived until the end of the Cretaceous.

FOSSIL OF A LATE JURASSIC PTEROSAUR
(*Pterodactylus kochi*)

PTERODACTYLUS

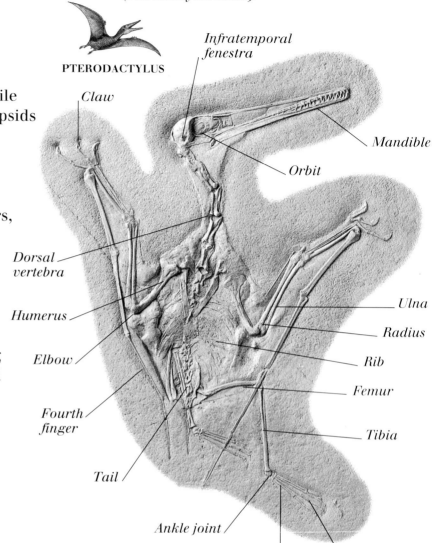

Claw

Infratemporal fenestra

Orbit

Mandible

Dorsal vertebra

Humerus

Elbow

Fourth finger

Tail

Ankle joint

Metatarsal

Ulna

Radius

Rib

Femur

Tibia

Phalanx

FEATURES OF AN EARLY TRIASSIC THECODONT
(*Euparkeria capensis*)
Length: 50 cm (20 in)

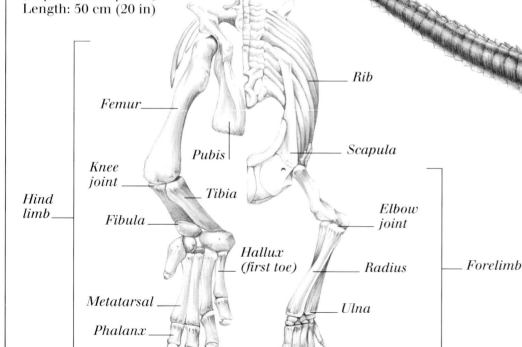

Femur

Rib

Pubis

Scapula

Knee joint

Tibia

Hind limb

Fibula

Elbow joint

Hallux (first toe)

Radius

Metatarsal

Ulna

Forelimb

Phalanx

HIND LIMB AND FORELIMB OF *EUPARKERIA*

Caudal vertebra

Iliofibularis muscle

Femur

Fibula

Tibia

Metatarsal

Phalanx

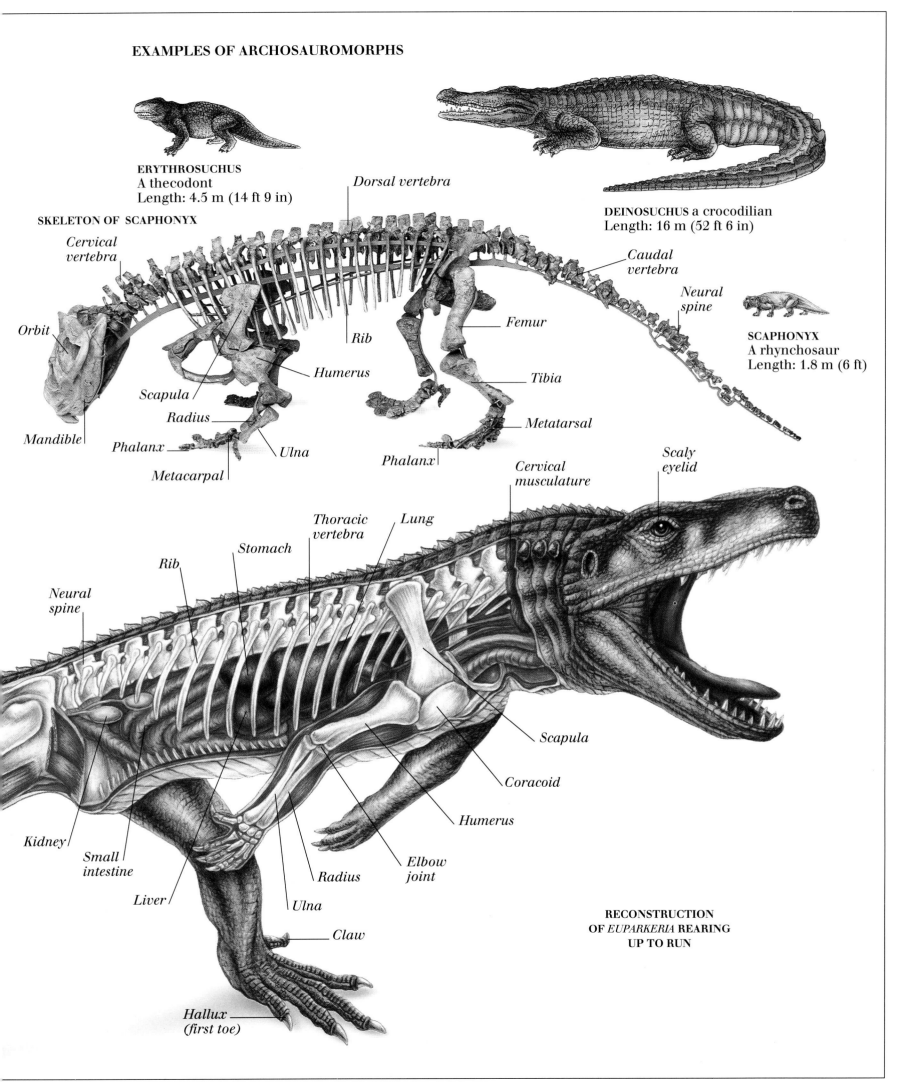

EXAMPLES OF ARCHOSAUROMORPHS

ERYTHROSUCHUS
A thecodont
Length: 4.5 m (14 ft 9 in)

Dorsal vertebra

DEINOSUCHUS a crocodilian
Length: 16 m (52 ft 6 in)

SKELETON OF SCAPHONYX

Cervical vertebra

Caudal vertebra

Neural spine

Orbit

SCAPHONYX
A rhynchosaur
Length: 1.8 m (6 ft)

Femur

Rib

Humerus

Tibia

Scapula

Radius

Metatarsal

Mandible

Phalanx

Ulna

Phalanx

Metacarpal

Scaly eyelid

Cervical musculature

Thoracic vertebra

Lung

Stomach

Rib

Neural spine

Scapula

Coracoid

Humerus

Kidney

Small intestine

Radius

Elbow joint

Liver

Ulna

RECONSTRUCTION OF *EUPARKERIA* REARING UP TO RUN

Claw

Hallux (first toe)

Saurischian dinosaurs

DINOSAURS WERE THE DOMINANT LAND ANIMALS from Late Triassic to Late Cretaceous times (about 225–65 million years ago). They are classified as a subdivision of the archosaurs (see pp. 38–39), distinguished by their upright stance (unlike that of most archosaurs) and various details of skull and limb bones. Dinosaurs are divided into saurischians, in which the pubes (a pair of bones in the hip girdle) typically slanted forwards, and ornithischians, in which the same bones slanted back. Saurischians in turn are divided into theropods and sauropodomorphs. Theropods, which included all predatory dinosaurs, ranged in size from the chicken-sized *Compsognathus* to the 15 m (49 ft) long, sail-backed *Spinosaurus*. Other examples are *Tyrannosaurus rex* and the bird-like *Avimimus*. Sauropodomorphs include the largest land animals ever to have lived, and fall into two groups: the prosauropods and their immense successors, the sauropods, such as the 21 m (69 ft) long *Apatosaurus*.

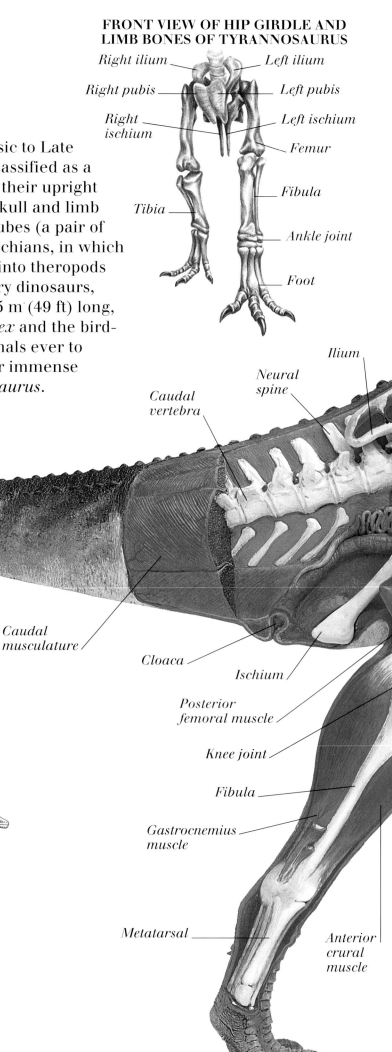

FRONT VIEW OF HIP GIRDLE AND LIMB BONES OF TYRANNOSAURUS

Right ilium
Left ilium
Right pubis
Left pubis
Right ischium
Left ischium
Femur
Fibula
Tibia
Ankle joint
Foot

Ilium
Neural spine
Caudal vertebra
Tail
Caudal musculature
Cloaca
Ischium
Posterior femoral muscle
Knee joint
Fibula
Gastrocnemius muscle
Metatarsal
Anterior crural muscle

EXAMPLES OF SAURISCHIAN DINOSAURS

AVIMIMUS
A Late Cretaceous theropod
Length: 1.5 m (5 ft)

SPINOSAURUS
A Middle Cretaceous theropod
Length: 15 m (49 ft)

APATOSAURUS
A Late Jurassic sauropod
Length: 21 m (69 ft)

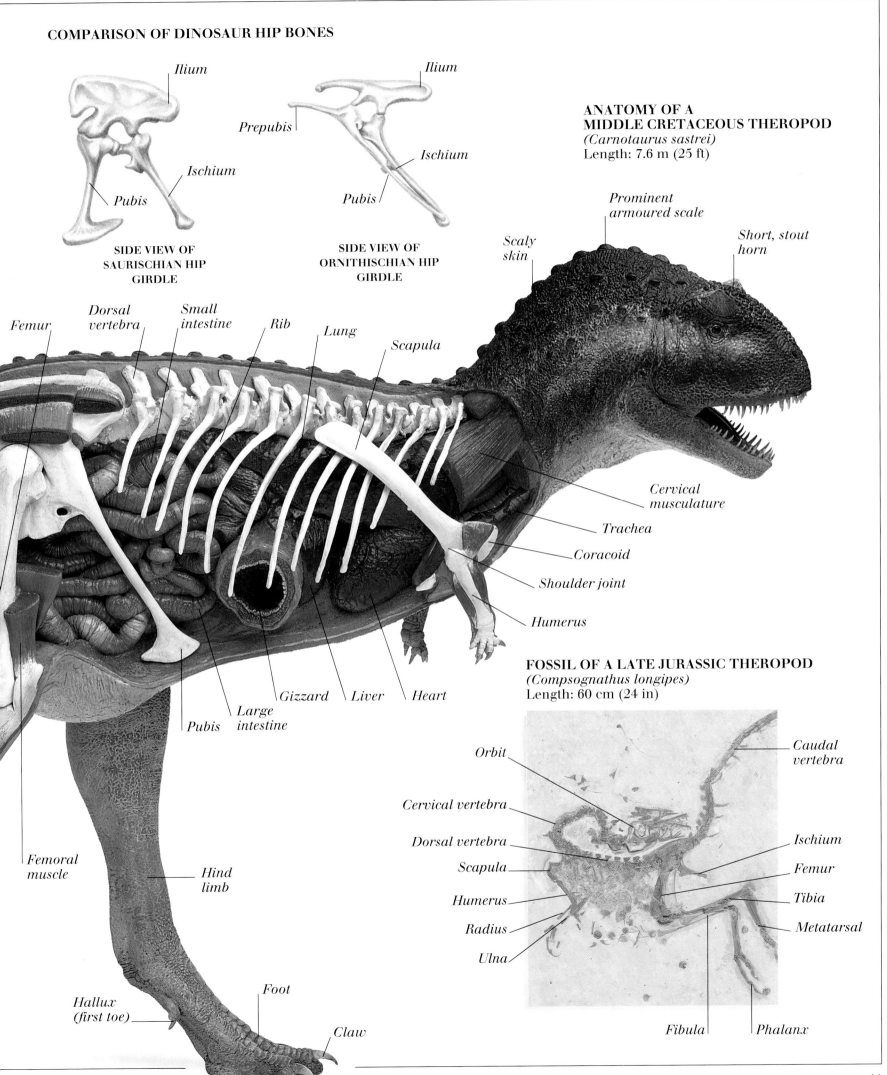

COMPARISON OF DINOSAUR HIP BONES

Ilium

Ischium

Pubis

**SIDE VIEW OF
SAURISCHIAN HIP
GIRDLE**

Ilium

Prepubis

Ischium

Pubis

**SIDE VIEW OF
ORNITHISCHIAN HIP
GIRDLE**

ANATOMY OF A
MIDDLE CRETACEOUS THEROPOD
(Carnotaurus sastrei)
Length: 7.6 m (25 ft)

Prominent
armoured scale

Short, stout
horn

Scaly
skin

Femur

Dorsal
vertebra

Small
intestine

Rib

Lung

Scapula

Cervical
musculature

Trachea

Coracoid

Shoulder joint

Humerus

Pubis

Large
intestine

Gizzard

Liver

Heart

Femoral
muscle

Hind
limb

Hallux
(first toe)

Foot

Claw

FOSSIL OF A LATE JURASSIC THEROPOD
(Compsognathus longipes)
Length: 60 cm (24 in)

Orbit

Caudal
vertebra

Cervical vertebra

Dorsal vertebra

Ischium

Scapula

Femur

Humerus

Tibia

Radius

Metatarsal

Ulna

Fibula

Phalanx

Ornithischian dinosaurs

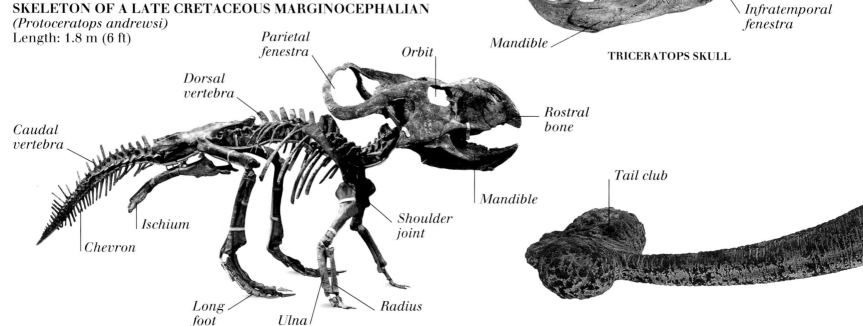
TUOJIANGOSAURUS
A thyreophoran

THE ORNITHISCHIANS WERE HERBIVOROUS dinosaurs, with teeth and jaws adapted to their diet. Most had a toothless beak for cropping leaves, cheek pouches in which to store them, and cheek teeth for chewing them. There are three ornithischian sub-orders: ornithopods, thyreophorans, and marginocephalians. Ornithopods included some species that ran on their hind legs, at least for some of the time. Among these was the hadrosaur *Parasaurolophus*, which had a backswept bony head crest containing a trombone-like airway that allowed the 10 m (33 ft) long herbivore to emit loud calls. Thyreophorans comprised the stegosaurs and ankylosaurs. Stegosaurs, such as the 7 m (23 ft) long *Tuojiangosaurus*, bore two rows of spikes or plates jutting up from the neck, back, and tail. Ankylosaurs ranged in size from the 3 m (10 ft) long *Minmi* to the heavily armoured, 7 m (23 ft) long *Euoplocephalus*, which possessed a bony tail club. Marginocephalians had a narrow shelf or deep bony frill at the back of the skull, and comprised two groups: pachycephalosaurs, such as *Stegoceras*, and ceratopsians, such as *Psittacosaurus* and the 1.8 m (6 ft) long *Protoceratops*. The largest ceratopsian was *Triceratops*, a three-horned, rhinoceros-like dinosaur measuring 9 m (29 ft 6 in) in length.

SKULLS OF MARGINOCEPHALIANS

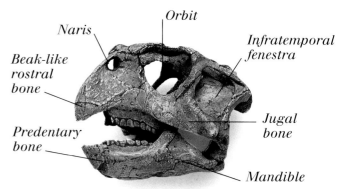

Naris

Orbit

Infratemporal fenestra

Beak-like rostral bone

Predentary bone

Jugal bone

Mandible

PSITTACOSAURUS SKULL

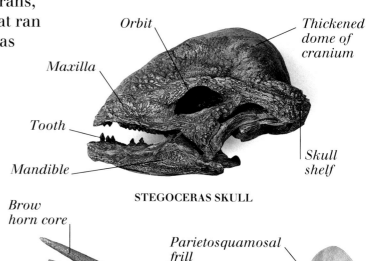

Orbit

Thickened dome of cranium

Maxilla

Tooth

Mandible

Skull shelf

STEGOCERAS SKULL

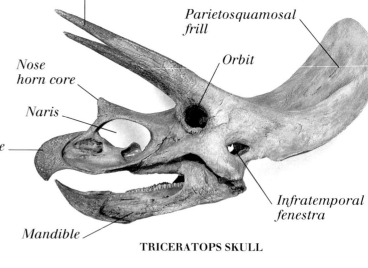

Brow horn core

Parietosquamosal frill

Nose horn core

Orbit

Naris

Rostral bone

Infratemporal fenestra

Mandible

TRICERATOPS SKULL

SKELETON OF A LATE CRETACEOUS MARGINOCEPHALIAN
(*Protoceratops andrewsi*)
Length: 1.8 m (6 ft)

Parietal fenestra

Orbit

Dorsal vertebra

Caudal vertebra

Rostral bone

Mandible

Ischium

Chevron

Shoulder joint

Long foot

Ulna

Radius

Tail club

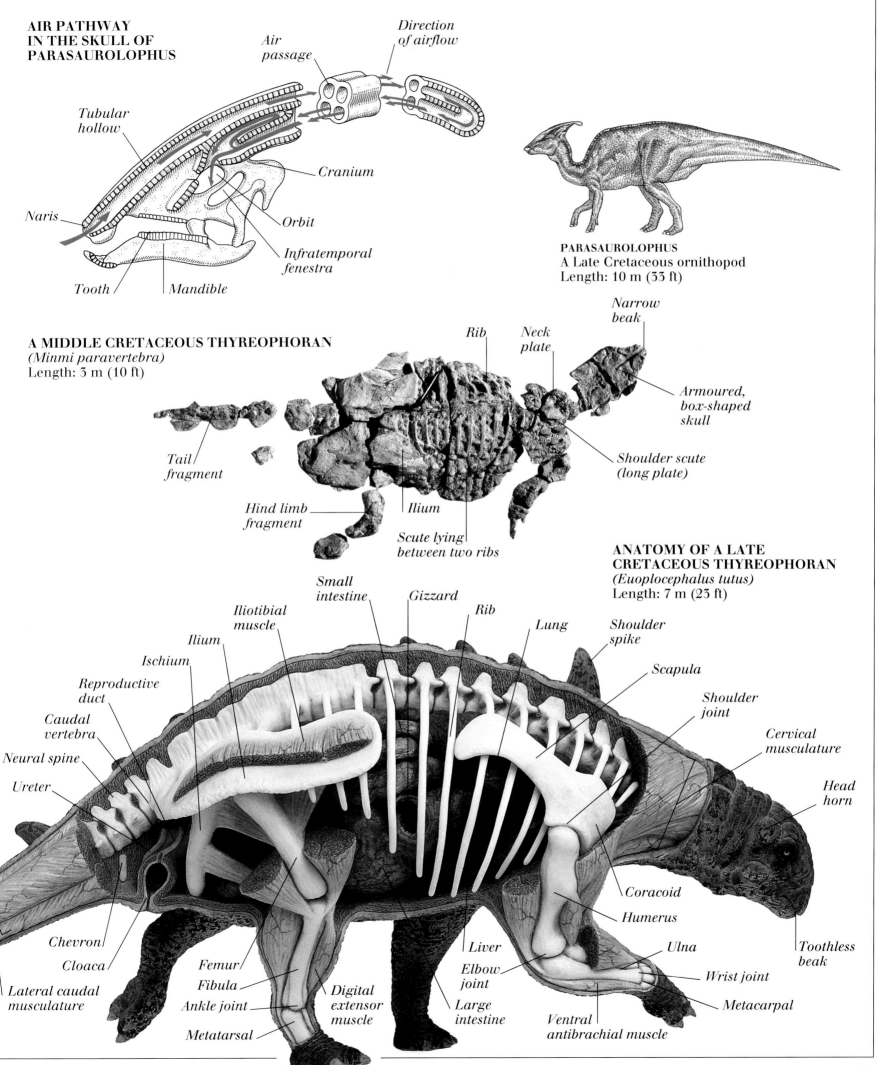

AIR PATHWAY IN THE SKULL OF PARASAUROLOPHUS

Air passage

Direction of airflow

Tubular hollow

Cranium

Naris

Orbit

Infratemporal fenestra

Tooth

Mandible

PARASAUROLOPHUS
A Late Cretaceous ornithopod
Length: 10 m (33 ft)

A MIDDLE CRETACEOUS THYREOPHORAN
(Minmi paravertebra)
Length: 3 m (10 ft)

Rib

Neck plate

Narrow beak

Armoured, box-shaped skull

Tail fragment

Shoulder scute (long plate)

Hind limb fragment

Ilium

Scute lying between two ribs

ANATOMY OF A LATE CRETACEOUS THYREOPHORAN
(Euoplocephalus tutus)
Length: 7 m (23 ft)

Small intestine

Gizzard

Iliotibial muscle

Rib

Lung

Shoulder spike

Ilium

Scapula

Ischium

Shoulder joint

Reproductive duct

Cervical musculature

Caudal vertebra

Neural spine

Ureter

Head horn

Coracoid

Humerus

Chevron

Liver

Ulna

Toothless beak

Cloaca

Elbow joint

Wrist joint

Lateral caudal musculature

Femur

Large intestine

Metacarpal

Fibula

Ventral antibrachial muscle

Ankle joint

Digital extensor muscle

Metatarsal

The earliest birds

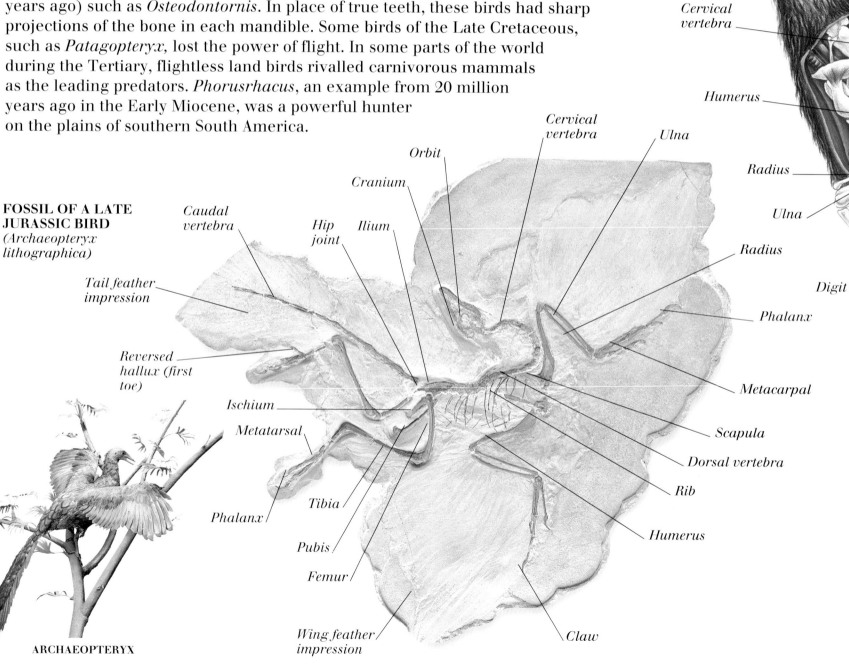

THE EARLIEST KNOWN BIRD was *Archaeopteryx*, which was the size of a modern crow and lived in the Late Jurassic, 150 million years ago. It is believed to be descended from the maniraptorans, a group of small theropod dinosaurs with particularly lightweight, agile bodies. The main apparent difference was that *Archaeopteryx* was covered in feathers. So close is the similarity in other respects that it is claimed that birds are living, flying dinosaurs. *Archaeopteryx* had the small, sharp teeth, the clawed fingers, and the long, bony tail core of a maniraptoran. Teeth persisted in some birds of the Cretaceous period (144–65 million years ago): *Ichthyornis*, a bird resembling a modern tern, and *Hesperornis*, a large diving bird. No toothed bird has existed since the Cretaceous, the nearest equivalent being the "bony-toothed" birds of the Tertiary period (65–2 million years ago) such as *Osteodontornis*. In place of true teeth, these birds had sharp projections of the bone in each mandible. Some birds of the Late Cretaceous, such as *Patagopteryx*, lost the power of flight. In some parts of the world during the Tertiary, flightless land birds rivalled carnivorous mammals as the leading predators. *Phorusrhacus*, an example from 20 million years ago in the Early Miocene, was a powerful hunter on the plains of southern South America.

ICHTHYORNIS

Scaly eye ring

Upper mandible

Ear

Lower mandible

Bare skin

Cervical vertebra

Humerus

Radius

Ulna

Digit

FOSSIL OF A LATE JURASSIC BIRD
(*Archaeopteryx lithographica*)

Caudal vertebra

Orbit

Cranium

Cervical vertebra

Ulna

Hip joint

Ilium

Radius

Tail feather impression

Phalanx

Reversed hallux (first toe)

Metacarpal

Ischium

Scapula

Metatarsal

Dorsal vertebra

Rib

Phalanx

Tibia

Humerus

Pubis

Femur

Wing feather impression

Claw

ARCHAEOPTERYX

SKULLS OF TOOTHED AND BONY-TOOTHED BIRDS

Prefrontal
Frontal
Narial opening
Postorbital
Maxilla
Premaxilla
Orbit
Tooth
Dentary
Articular bone

ARCHAEOPTERYX
A toothed bird

Orbit
Frontal
Maxilla
Parietal bone
Premaxilla
Bony extension of mandible
Dentary
Articular bone

OSTEODONTORNIS
A bony-toothed bird

Antorbital fenestra
Frontal
Parietal bone
Narial opening
Premaxilla
Tooth
Maxilla
Orbit
Dentary
Articular bone

HESPERORNIS
A toothed bird

FEATURES OF A MIOCENE FLIGHTLESS LAND BIRD
(*Phorusrhacus inflatus*)

Frontal
Orbit
Cranium
Naris
Hooked beak
Maxilla

FOSSIL SKULL

Scapula
Lung
Dorsal vertebra
Rib
Gizzard
Ilium
Femur
Posterior femoral muscle
Cloaca
Heart
Large intestine
Pubis
Femoral muscle
Anterior crural muscle
Posterior crural muscle
Tail feather
Tibiotarsus
Tendon
Claw
Tarsometatarsal
Digit

**A FLIGHTLESS LAND BIRD
FROM THE CRETACEOUS**
(*Patagopteryx deferrariisi*)

PHORUSRHACUS
Length: 1.5 m (5 ft)

Primitive mammals

DIPROTODON

MAMMALS ARE WARM-BLOODED, often hairy vertebrates whose females produce milk for their young. They appeared about 220 million years ago, in the Late Triassic, soon after the first dinosaurs. Fossils of early mammals can be distinguished from those of therapsid reptiles (see pp. 34–35) by distinctive bones of the jaw and middle ear. The earliest mammals resembled shrews and developed multi-cusped teeth (with several points or cusps) that sheared through food as they chewed. One group of primitive mammals, the monotremes, laid eggs and is represented today by the platypus and the spiny anteaters. Most fossil and living mammals belong to the subclass Theria, which give birth to live young. Before the death of the dinosaurs (65 million years ago), two groups of Theria appeared, marsupials (pouched mammals) which produce tiny, underdeveloped young, and placentals which give birth to well-developed babies, nourished in their mother's womb by a placenta. Pleistocene marsupials included the hippopotamus-sized *Diprotodon* from Australia, and the still-living opossums (family Didelphidae) from the Americas. Extinct Pleistocene placentals included the ground sloth *Megatherium*, and the giant armadillo *Glyptodon*, both from South America. Both are edentates, a primitive group that includes modern armadillos, anteaters, and sloths.

PLEISTOCENE PLACENTAL
(Megatherium americanum)
Length: 6 m (19 ft 6 in)

FEATURES OF A PLEISTOCENE EDENTATE
(Glyptodon reticulatus)
Length: 2 m (6 ft 6 in)

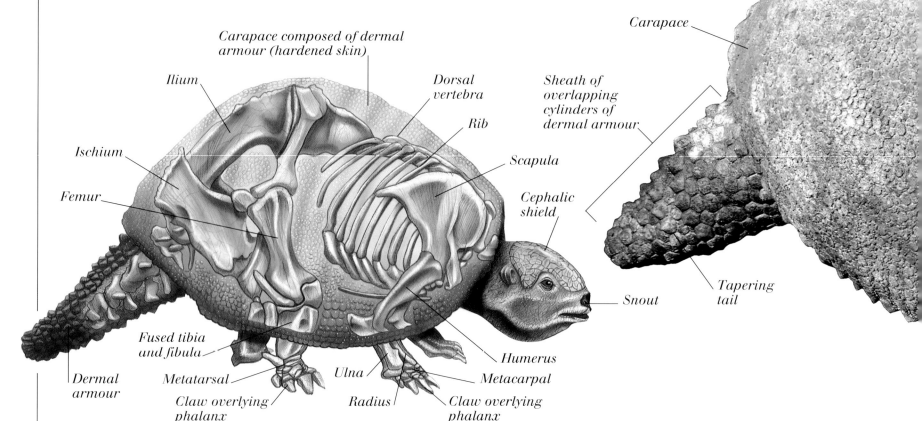

Carapace composed of dermal armour (hardened skin)

Ilium

Dorsal vertebra

Rib

Ischium

Scapula

Femur

Sheath of overlapping cylinders of dermal armour

Carapace

Cephalic shield

Snout

Tapering tail

Fused tibia and fibula

Humerus

Dermal armour

Metatarsal

Ulna

Metacarpal

Claw overlying phalanx

Radius

Claw overlying phalanx

INTERNAL VIEW SHOWING SKELETON

EXAMPLES OF PRIMITIVE MAMMALS

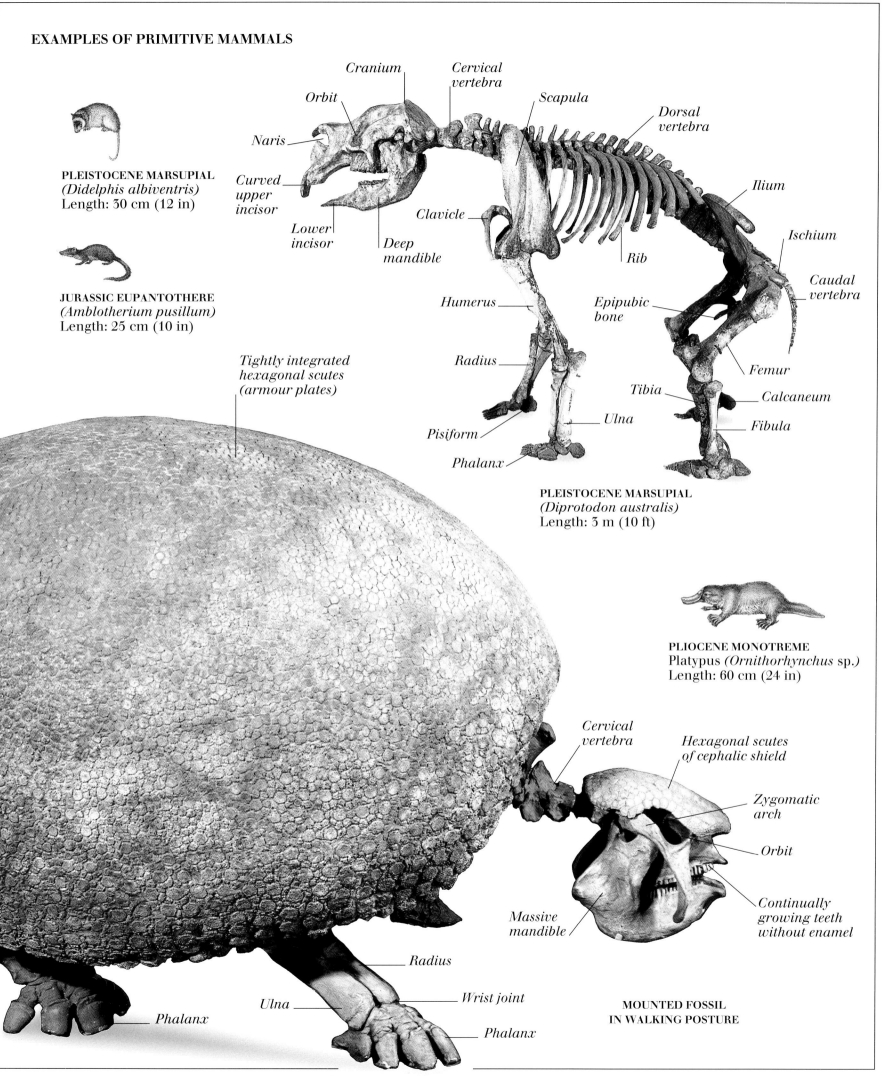

PLEISTOCENE MARSUPIAL
(Didelphis albiventris)
Length: 30 cm (12 in)

JURASSIC EUPANTOTHERE
(Amblotherium pusillum)
Length: 25 cm (10 in)

Cranium

Cervical
vertebra

Orbit

Scapula

Dorsal
vertebra

Naris

Curved
upper
incisor

Ilium

Clavicle

Ischium

Lower
incisor

Deep
mandible

Rib

Caudal
vertebra

Humerus

Epipubic
bone

Radius

Femur

Tibia

Calcaneum

Ulna

Fibula

Pisiform

Phalanx

PLEISTOCENE MARSUPIAL
(Diprotodon australis)
Length: 3 m (10 ft)

*Tightly integrated
hexagonal scutes
(armour plates)*

PLIOCENE MONOTREME
Platypus *(Ornithorhynchus sp.)*
Length: 60 cm (24 in)

Cervical
vertebra

Hexagonal scutes
of cephalic shield

Zygomatic
arch

Orbit

Continually
growing teeth
without enamel

Massive
mandible

Radius

Wrist joint

**MOUNTED FOSSIL
IN WALKING POSTURE**

Ulna

Phalanx

Phalanx

Carnivorous mammals

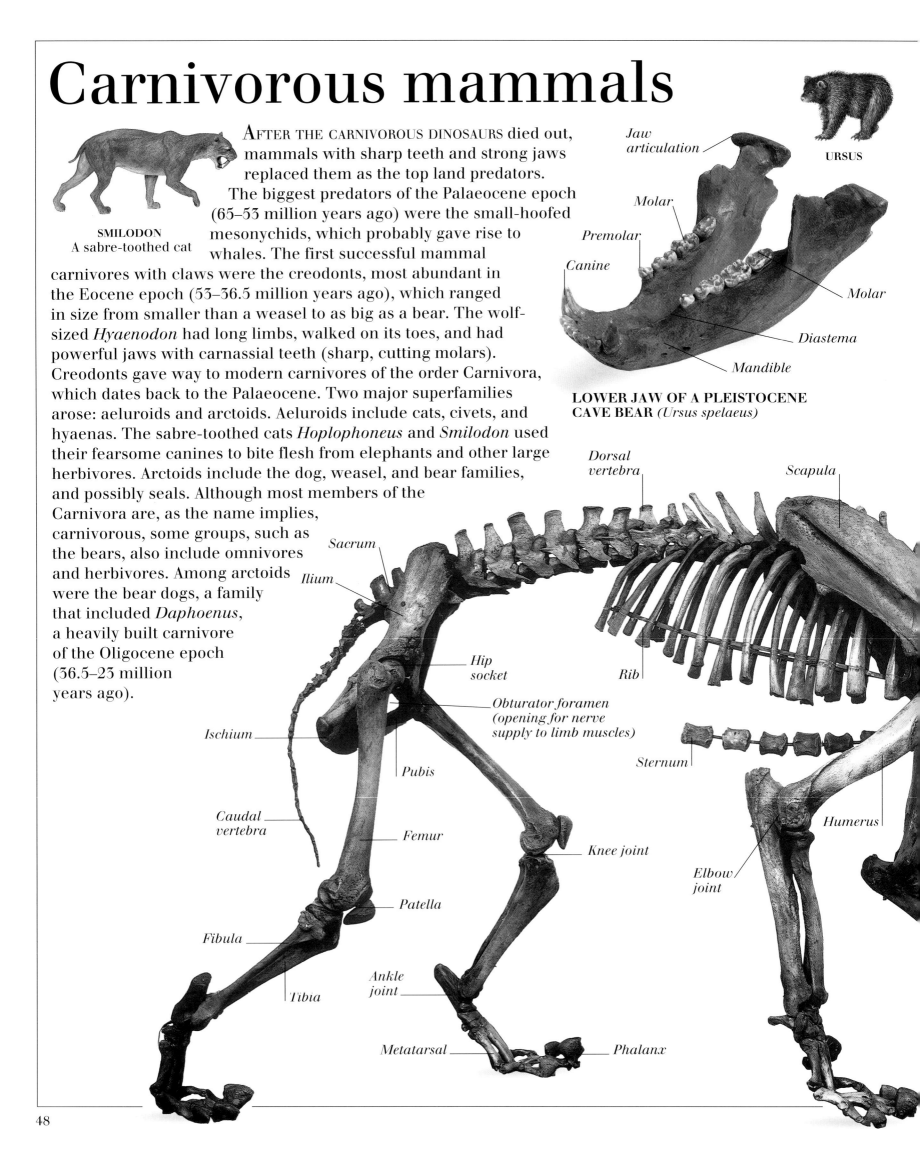

AFTER THE CARNIVOROUS DINOSAURS died out, mammals with sharp teeth and strong jaws replaced them as the top land predators. The biggest predators of the Palaeocene epoch (65–53 million years ago) were the small-hoofed mesonychids, which probably gave rise to whales. The first successful mammal carnivores with claws were the creodonts, most abundant in the Eocene epoch (53–36.5 million years ago), which ranged in size from smaller than a weasel to as big as a bear. The wolf-sized *Hyaenodon* had long limbs, walked on its toes, and had powerful jaws with carnassial teeth (sharp, cutting molars). Creodonts gave way to modern carnivores of the order Carnivora, which dates back to the Palaeocene. Two major superfamilies arose: aeluroids and arctoids. Aeluroids include cats, civets, and hyaenas. The sabre-toothed cats *Hoplophoneus* and *Smilodon* used their fearsome canines to bite flesh from elephants and other large herbivores. Arctoids include the dog, weasel, and bear families, and possibly seals. Although most members of the Carnivora are, as the name implies, carnivorous, some groups, such as the bears, also include omnivores and herbivores. Among arctoids were the bear dogs, a family that included *Daphoenus*, a heavily built carnivore of the Oligocene epoch (36.5–23 million years ago).

SMILODON
A sabre-toothed cat

URSUS

Jaw articulation

Molar

Premolar

Canine

Molar

Diastema

Mandible

LOWER JAW OF A PLEISTOCENE CAVE BEAR (*Ursus spelaeus*)

Dorsal vertebra

Scapula

Sacrum

Ilium

Hip socket

Rib

Obturator foramen (opening for nerve supply to limb muscles)

Ischium

Sternum

Pubis

Knee joint

Humerus

Caudal vertebra

Femur

Elbow joint

Patella

Fibula

Ankle joint

Tibia

Metatarsal

Phalanx

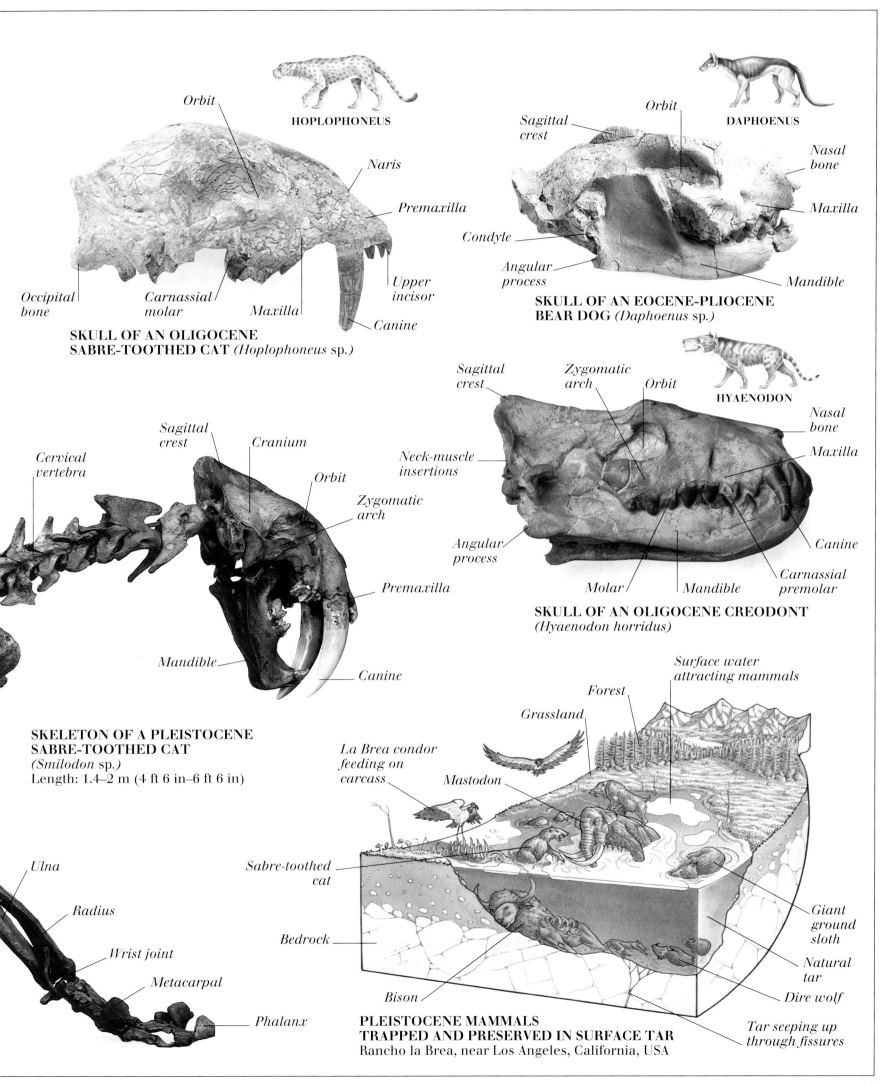

HOPLOPHONEUS

Orbit

Naris

Premaxilla

Upper incisor

Canine

Occipital bone

Carnassial molar

Maxilla

**SKULL OF AN OLIGOCENE
SABRE-TOOTHED CAT** (*Hoplophoneus* sp.)

DAPHOENUS

Orbit

Sagittal crest

Nasal bone

Maxilla

Condyle

Angular process

Mandible

**SKULL OF AN EOCENE-PLIOCENE
BEAR DOG** (*Daphoenus* sp.)

Sagittal crest

Cranium

Cervical vertebra

Orbit

Zygomatic arch

Premaxilla

Mandible

Canine

**SKELETON OF A PLEISTOCENE
SABRE-TOOTHED CAT**
(*Smilodon* sp.)
Length: 1.4–2 m (4 ft 6 in–6 ft 6 in)

Sagittal crest

Zygomatic arch

Orbit

HYAENODON

Nasal bone

Maxilla

Neck-muscle insertions

Angular process

Molar

Mandible

Canine

Carnassial premolar

SKULL OF AN OLIGOCENE CREODONT
(*Hyaenodon horridus*)

Ulna

Radius

Wrist joint

Metacarpal

Phalanx

Surface water attracting mammals

Forest

Grassland

La Brea condor feeding on carcass

Mastodon

Sabre-toothed cat

Bedrock

Bison

Giant ground sloth

Natural tar

Dire wolf

Tar seeping up through fissures

**PLEISTOCENE MAMMALS
TRAPPED AND PRESERVED IN SURFACE TAR**
Rancho la Brea, near Los Angeles, California, USA

49

Hoofed mammals

HYRACOTHERIUM

THE HOOFED MAMMALS, OR UNGULATES, are herbivores derived from small, fleet-footed ancestors that ran on tiptoe to escape from predators. Ungulates developed long upper foot bones and tended to lose outer toes, sacrificing claws to gain broad, weight-bearing hooves. Two main groups arose: the perissodactyls or odd-toed ungulates, and the artiodactyls or even-toed ungulates; both appeared in the Eocene epoch (53–36.5 million years ago). An early perissodactyl was the fox-sized *Hyracotherium*, the first known horse. In the Oligocene epoch (36.5–23 million years ago), perissodactyls reached enormous sizes: *Brontotherium* was 4 m (13 ft) long, and the hornless giant rhinoceros *Paraceratherium* weighed up to 20 tonnes and was possibly the heaviest ever land mammal. The 4 m (13 ft) long woolly rhinoceros *Coelodonta* had a shaggy coat adapted for survival in the glacial phases of the Pleistocene (2 million–10,000 years ago). Artiodactyls evolved in great variety: the Oligocene mammals *Cainotherium* and *Merycoidodon* were distant relatives of camels, and the moose-like *Sivatherium* from the Pliocene (5.5–2 million years ago) was an early relative of the giraffe. The present-day bison also dates back to the Pliocene. In South America, which was an island between roughly 73 and 3 million years ago, several groups of hoofed mammals developed, including the notoungulates. The last survivor of these was the rhinoceros-sized *Toxodon*, which flourished in the Pleistocene.

EXAMPLES OF PERISSODACTYLS

COELODONTA
A Miocene-Pleistocene woolly rhinoceros
Length: 4 m (13 ft)

BRONTOTHERIUM
An Oligocene brontothere
Length: 4 m (13 ft)

PARACERATHERIUM
An Oligocene hornless rhinoceros
Length: 7 m (23 ft)

TOXODON
A Pleistocene notoungulate
Length: 3 m (10 ft)

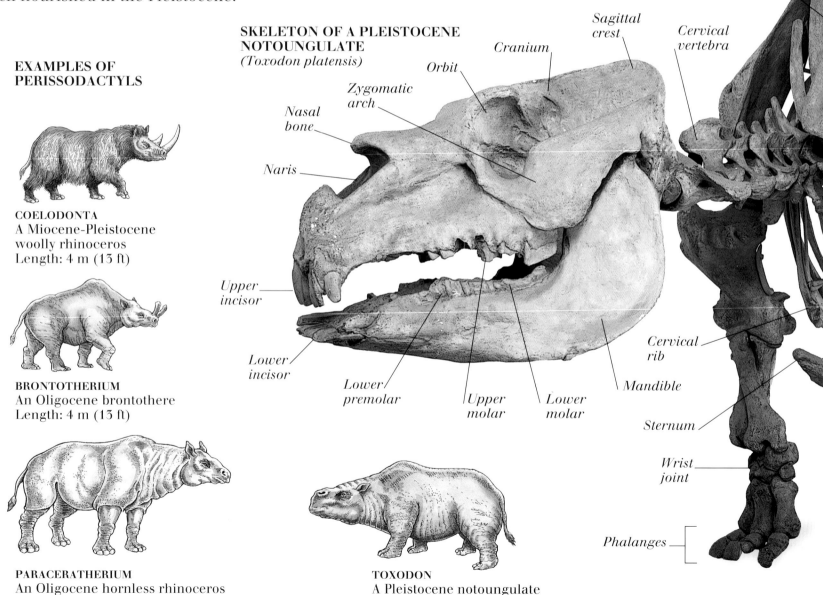

SKELETON OF A PLEISTOCENE NOTOUNGULATE
(Toxodon platensis)

Scapula

Sagittal crest

Cervical vertebra

Cranium

Orbit

Zygomatic arch

Nasal bone

Naris

Upper incisor

Lower incisor

Lower premolar

Upper molar

Lower molar

Mandible

Cervical rib

Sternum

Wrist joint

Phalanges

EXAMPLES OF ARTIODACTYLS

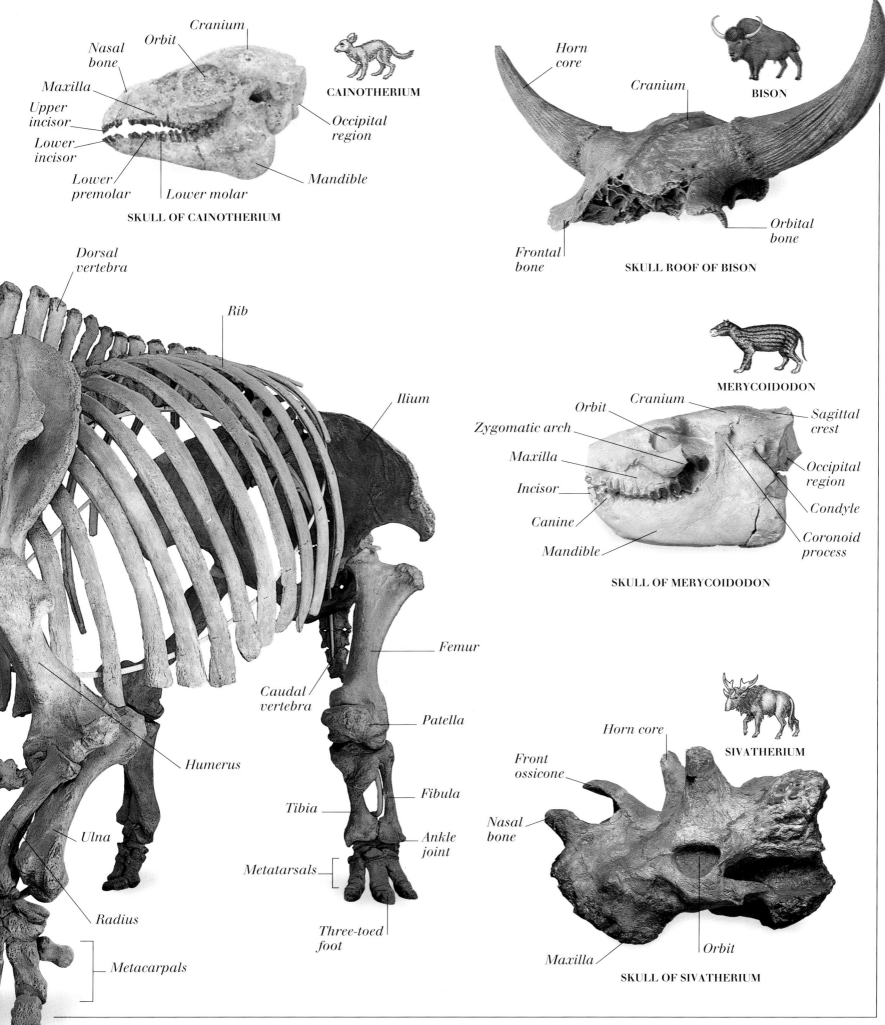

SKULL OF CAINOTHERIUM

Cranium

Orbit

Nasal bone

Maxilla

Upper incisor

Lower incisor

Lower premolar

Lower molar

CAINOTHERIUM

Occipital region

Mandible

SKULL ROOF OF BISON

Horn core

Cranium

BISON

Orbital bone

Frontal bone

Dorsal vertebra

Rib

Ilium

Femur

Caudal vertebra

Patella

Humerus

Fibula

Tibia

Ankle joint

Ulna

Metatarsals

Radius

Three-toed foot

Metacarpals

SKULL OF MERYCOIDODON

MERYCOIDODON

Cranium

Orbit

Zygomatic arch

Sagittal crest

Maxilla

Occipital region

Incisor

Condyle

Canine

Coronoid process

Mandible

SKULL OF SIVATHERIUM

SIVATHERIUM

Horn core

Front ossicone

Nasal bone

Maxilla

Orbit

Elephants and their kin

THE TWO LIVING SPECIES OF ELEPHANT – African and Indian – are the only surviving representatives of the proboscideans, a group that was widespread throughout much of the Cenozoic era. One of the first proboscideans was *Moeritherium*. A herbivore from Oligocene Africa, it had small molars, rudimentary tusks, and a long upper lip that foreshadowed an elephant's fleshy trunk. Tusks developed as extensions of the incisor teeth; some of the proboscideans, notably the gomphotheres, possessed two pairs. *Phiomia*, a horse-sized Oligocene gomphothere, had a small trunk, high-crowned molars, short upper tusks, and a pair of shovel-shaped tusks in the lower jaw. The Miocene *Gomphotherium* had equally long upper and lower tusks. Among later proboscideans was the Pliocene *Stegodon*, a 7 m (23 ft) long mammutoid with 3 m (10 ft) long upper tusks and one to three huge molars in each jaw. The oldest known fossil elephants are about 5 million years old and are found in Africa. Mammoths appeared earlier, and one of the most famous extinct elephants is the woolly mammoth, which had a thick insulating coat adapted for the extreme climatic conditions of the glacial phases of the Pleistocene epoch (2 million to 10,000 years ago). One theory for its demise is that it was hunted to extinction by early humans.

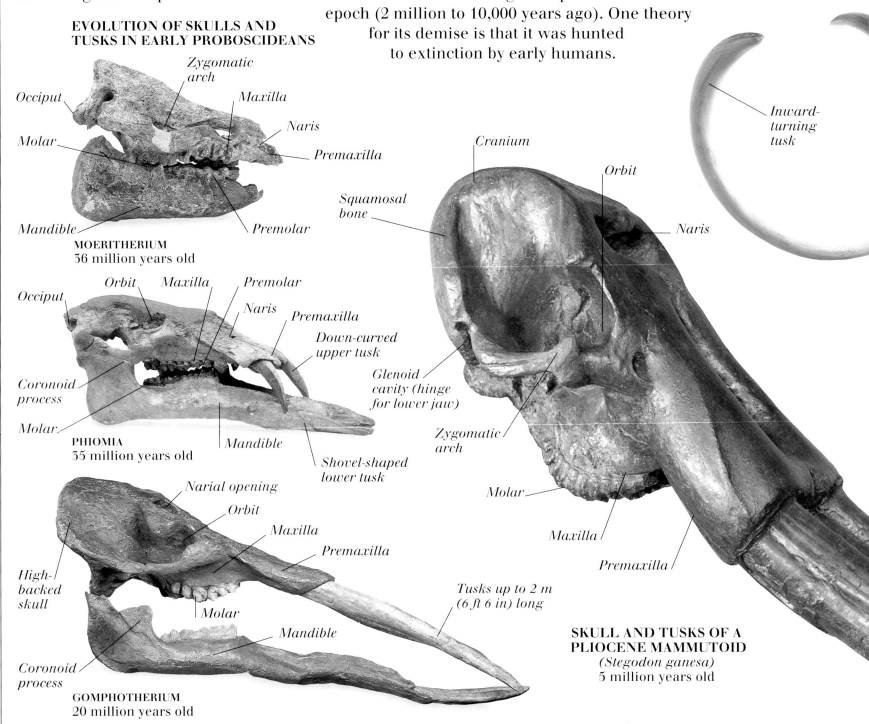

EVOLUTION OF SKULLS AND TUSKS IN EARLY PROBOSCIDEANS

Zygomatic arch

Occiput

Maxilla

Molar

Naris

Premaxilla

Mandible

Premolar

MOERITHERIUM
36 million years old

Occiput

Orbit

Maxilla

Premolar

Naris

Premaxilla

Down-curved upper tusk

Coronoid process

Molar

PHIOMIA
35 million years old

Mandible

Shovel-shaped lower tusk

Narial opening

Orbit

Maxilla

Premaxilla

High-backed skull

Molar

Mandible

Coronoid process

GOMPHOTHERIUM
20 million years old

Cranium

Orbit

Squamosal bone

Naris

Glenoid cavity (hinge for lower jaw)

Zygomatic arch

Molar

Maxilla

Premaxilla

Inward-turning tusk

Tusks up to 2 m (6 ft 6 in) long

SKULL AND TUSKS OF A PLIOCENE MAMMUTOID
(Stegodon ganesa)
5 million years old

EXAMPLES OF PROBOSCIDEANS

Pinna (ear flap)

Rump

Long, flexible lip

Short leg

Belly

MOERITHERIUM
An Oligocene moerithere
Height: 1 m (3 ft 3 in)

Domed forehead

Pinna (ear flap)

Trunk

Short tusk (upper incisor)

Tail

Shovel-shaped tusk (lower incisor)

Belly

PHIOMIA
An Oligocene gomphothere
Height: 2.4 m (8 ft)

Flat forehead

Pinna (ear flap)

Tusk (upper incisor)

Tail

Belly

LOXODONTA
Modern African elephant
Height: 4 m (13 ft)

High cranium

Eye

Small ear

Arched back

Shoulder

Rump

Thigh

Thick insulating coat

Hind leg

Thick woolly underhair

Forelimb

Lower "lip"

Belly

Ankle

Hair-covered trunk

Heel

Foot

Upper "lip"

Toenail

FEATURES OF A PLEISTOCENE MAMMUTOID
Woolly mammoth (*Mammuthus primigenius*)
Height: 4 m (13 ft)

Tusks 3 m (10 ft) long

Primates

HUMANS, MONKEYS, APES, AND LEMURS are primates – agile animals originally adapted for living in trees. Apes and Old World monkeys sprang from creatures such as *Aegyptopithecus*, living in the Early Oligocene, some 36.5 million years ago. In the Late Miocene, about 6 million years ago, early apes gave rise to the family Hominidae, to which humans belong. Hominids, whose earliest known genus was *Australopithecus*, were the first primates to walk upright. The genus *Homo* (humans) evolved in the Pliocene, by 2.5 million years ago. Its first members (*Homo rudolfensis* and *Homo habilis*) were shorter than modern humans, and made chipped-stone tools. *Homo erectus* had appeared by 1.8 million years ago and, by 500,000 years ago, gave rise to *Homo sapiens*, whose subspecies include neanderthals and modern humans. Neanderthals lived from 200,000 to 30,000 years ago, spanning at least two of the Pleistocene's icy climatic phases. Modern humans had evolved in Africa by 100,000 years ago. With their more advanced hunting methods they colonized much of the world, and by 30,000 years ago they had driven the neanderthals into extinction.

RECONSTRUCTION OF
***AUSTRALOPITHECUS AFARENSIS* PAIR**
Male height: 1.45 m (4 ft 9 in)

FEATURES OF A PLIOCENE HOMINID
(*Australopithecus afarensis*)
3.18 million years ago

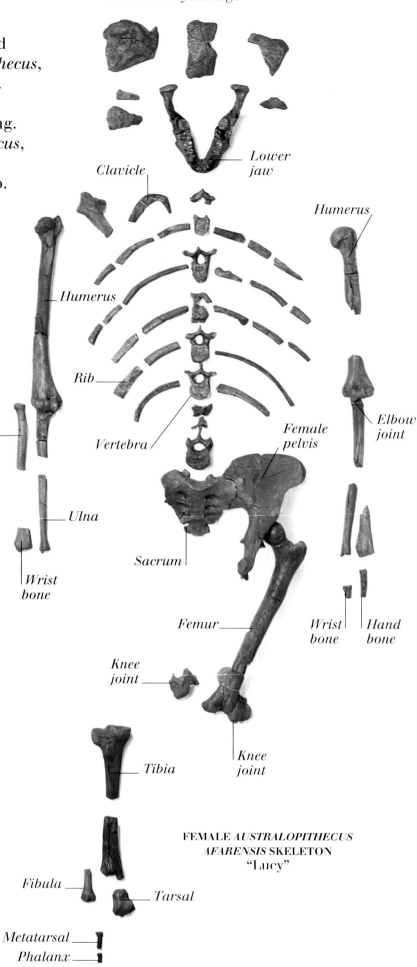

Clavicle

Lower jaw

Humerus

Humerus

Rib

Radius

Vertebra

Female pelvis

Elbow joint

Ulna

Sacrum

Wrist bone

Femur

Wrist bone

Hand bone

Knee joint

Knee joint

Tibia

**FEMALE *AUSTRALOPITHECUS
AFARENSIS* SKELETON
"Lucy"**

Fibula

Tarsal

Metatarsal

Phalanx

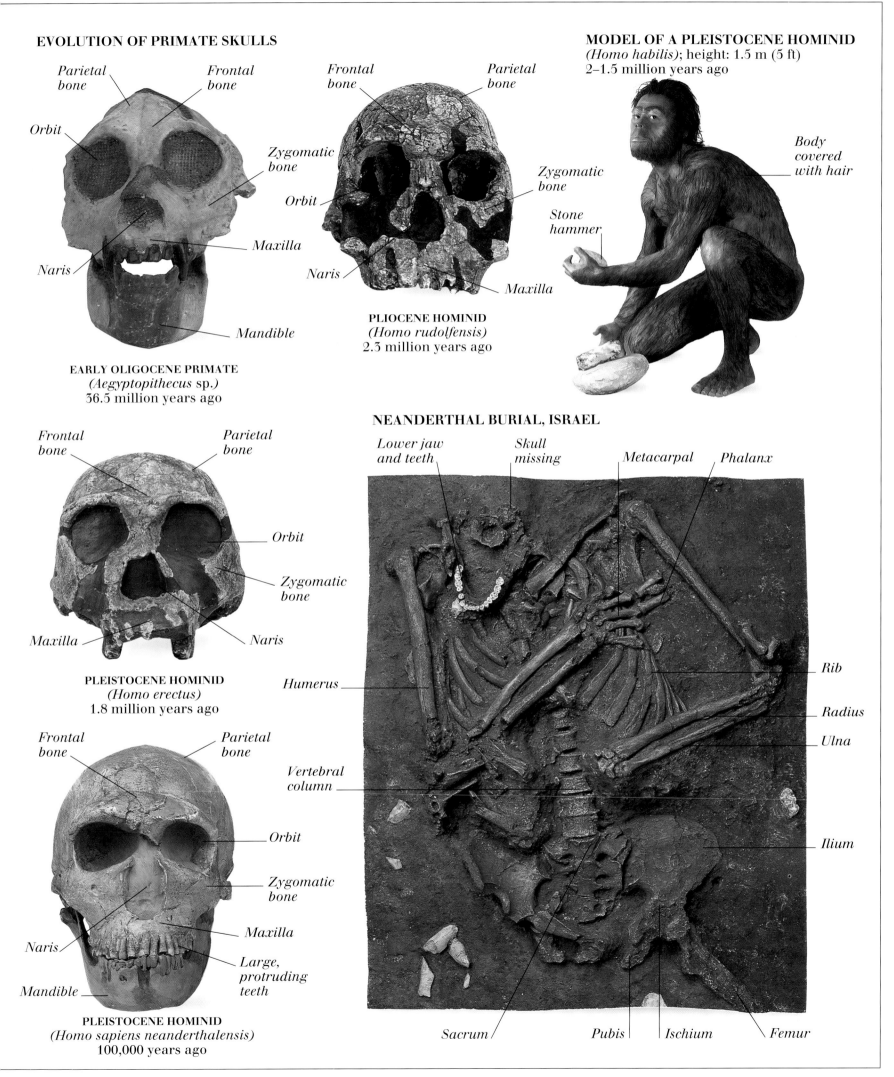

EVOLUTION OF PRIMATE SKULLS

Parietal bone

Frontal bone

Orbit

Zygomatic bone

Maxilla

Naris

Mandible

EARLY OLIGOCENE PRIMATE
(*Aegyptopithecus* sp.)
36.5 million years ago

Frontal bone

Parietal bone

Zygomatic bone

Orbit

Naris

Maxilla

PLIOCENE HOMINID
(*Homo rudolfensis*)
2.3 million years ago

MODEL OF A PLEISTOCENE HOMINID
(*Homo habilis*); height: 1.5 m (5 ft)
2–1.5 million years ago

Body covered with hair

Stone hammer

Frontal bone

Parietal bone

Orbit

Zygomatic bone

Maxilla

Naris

PLEISTOCENE HOMINID
(*Homo erectus*)
1.8 million years ago

Frontal bone

Parietal bone

Orbit

Zygomatic bone

Maxilla

Naris

Large, protruding teeth

Mandible

PLEISTOCENE HOMINID
(*Homo sapiens neanderthalensis*)
100,000 years ago

NEANDERTHAL BURIAL, ISRAEL

Lower jaw and teeth

Skull missing

Metacarpal

Phalanx

Humerus

Vertebral column

Rib

Radius

Ulna

Ilium

Sacrum

Pubis

Ischium

Femur

55

Time chart: animals

THE FIRST ANIMALS APPEARED in Precambrian time, evolving from animal-like members of the protist kingdom (single-celled organisms with a cell nucleus). During the Phanerozoic aeon (550 million years ago to the present), the main animal groups emerged and flourished, some becoming extinct. Insects have become the most diverse group of animals today, accounting for at least three-quarters of all living species. They far outstrip the mammals, which are generally considered the dominant animal group of modern time. This chart shows a selection of the main animal groups through geological time and indicates how they are related to one another. The widths of the coloured pathways broadly reflect the varying abundance of the animals in the groups. The colours of the pathways each correspond to a phylum (plural: phyla), a major unit of animal classification. Abrupt narrowings of the pathways reveal two of the most severe extinction events in the history of the animal kingdom, occurring at the end of the Permian and the Cretaceous periods. During each of these events, thousands of animal species became extinct.

KEY
INVERTEBRATES

- SPONGES
- CORALS, ETC.
- ANNELID WORMS
- ARTHROPODS
- MOLLUSCS
- BRYOZOANS
- BRACHIOPODS
- ECHINODERMS
- HEMICHORDATES

VERTEBRATES

- CHORDATES

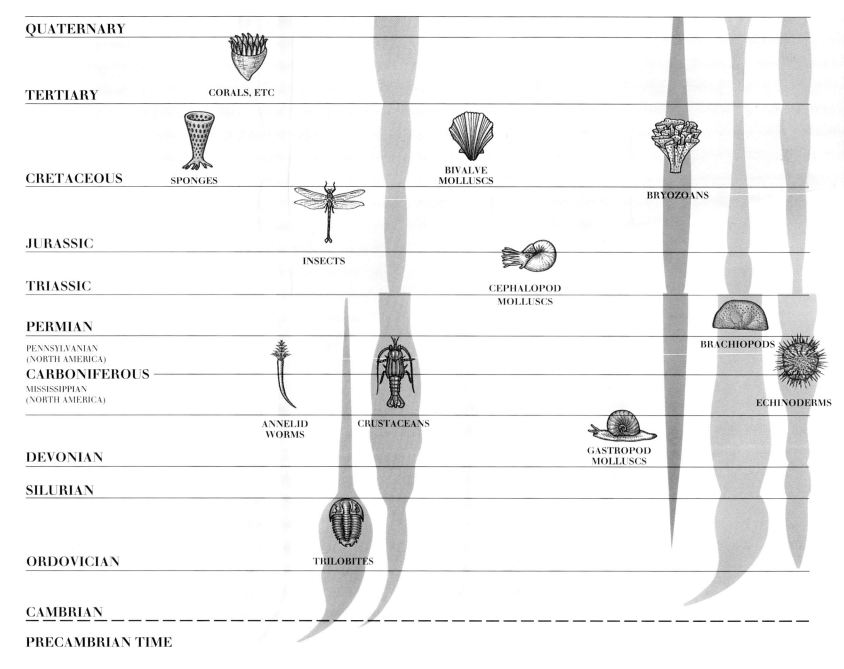

QUATERNARY

TERTIARY

CORALS, ETC

CRETACEOUS

SPONGES

BIVALVE MOLLUSCS

BRYOZOANS

INSECTS

JURASSIC

CEPHALOPOD MOLLUSCS

TRIASSIC

PERMIAN

PENNSYLVANIAN (NORTH AMERICA)

BRACHIOPODS

CARBONIFEROUS

MISSISSIPPIAN (NORTH AMERICA)

ECHINODERMS

ANNELID WORMS

CRUSTACEANS

GASTROPOD MOLLUSCS

DEVONIAN

SILURIAN

ORDOVICIAN

TRILOBITES

CAMBRIAN

PRECAMBRIAN TIME

EXAMPLES OF EXTINCT LIFE FORMS

TRILOBITE
A type of arthropod that flourished in shallow seas from the Cambrian (when it was the dominant life form) to the Permian period.

GRAPTOLITE
Sea-dwelling organisms that formed colonies, sometimes spiral in shape, and lived from the Cambrian to the Carboniferous period.

JAWLESS FISH
Apart from the 32 living species of hagfishes and lampreys, the jawless fishes died out by the end of the Devonian period.

SEA SCORPION
The sea scorpions were a group of arthropods, some as large as a human being, that died out during the Palaeozoic era.

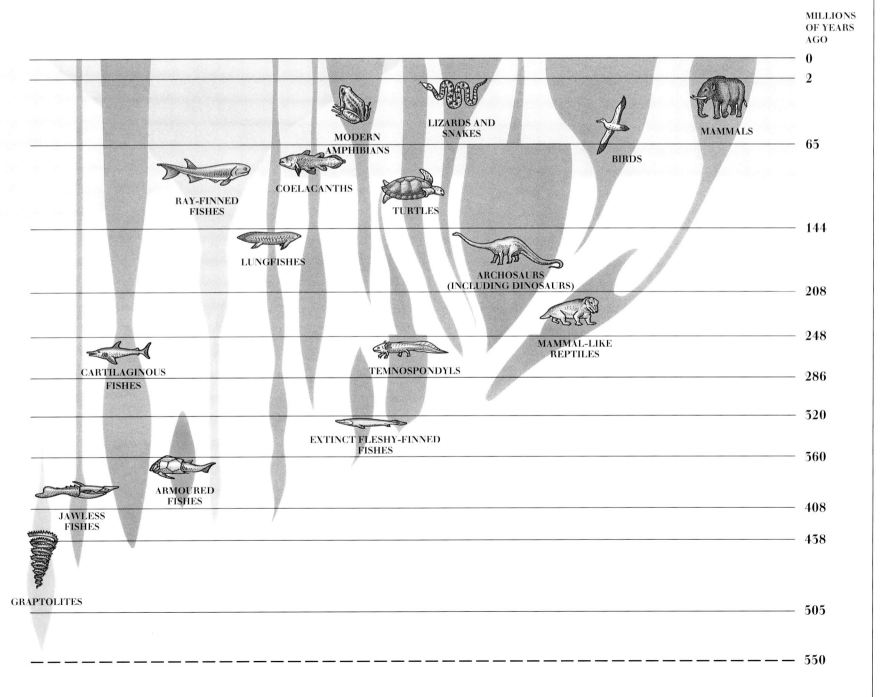

MILLIONS OF YEARS AGO

0

2

MODERN AMPHIBIANS

LIZARDS AND SNAKES

MAMMALS

BIRDS

65

COELACANTHS

RAY-FINNED FISHES

TURTLES

144

LUNGFISHES

ARCHOSAURS (INCLUDING DINOSAURS)

208

MAMMAL-LIKE REPTILES

248

CARTILAGINOUS FISHES

TEMNOSPONDYLS

286

320

EXTINCT FLESHY-FINNED FISHES

360

ARMOURED FISHES

408

JAWLESS FISHES

438

GRAPTOLITES

505

550

Time chart: plants

THE STORY OF THE PLANT KINGDOM begins with Precambrian algae and culminates in the present-day dominance of flowering plants, after their dramatic diversification in the middle of the Cretaceous period around 100 million years ago. This chart illustrates the changing pattern of the world's plant groups, as well as their origins and extinctions. The widths of the coloured pathways reflect the prominence of each group in the world's flora. The basic unit of plant classification is the division, and in general, each colour represents a division. One exception is the single colour that corresponds to the algae, of which there are several divisions. The algae are not shown to scale because many authorities consider that most of them are not plants, but protists (single-celled organisms with a nucleus) or colonies of protists.

KEY

	ALGAE
	BRYOPHYTES
	EARLY LAND PLANTS
	CLUBMOSSES
	CLADOXYLALES
	HORSETAILS
	FERNS
	PROGYMNOSPERMS
	GYMNOSPERMS
	FLOWERING PLANTS

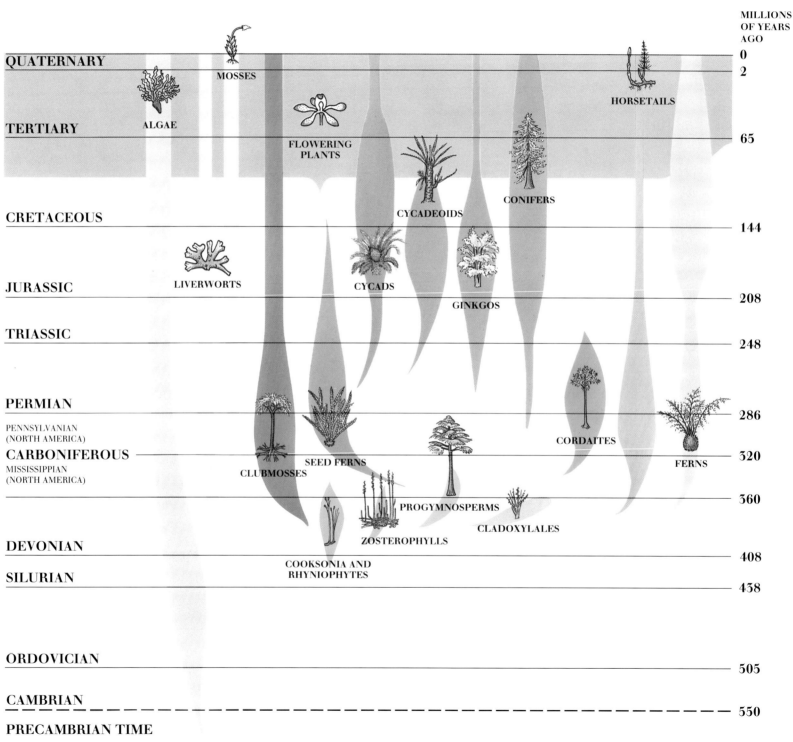

MILLIONS OF YEARS AGO

QUATERNARY — 0
— 2
MOSSES

HORSETAILS

ALGAE

TERTIARY — 65

FLOWERING PLANTS

CYCADEOIDS

CONIFERS

CRETACEOUS — 144

LIVERWORTS

CYCADS

JURASSIC — 208

GINKGOS

TRIASSIC — 248

PERMIAN — 286

CORDAITES

PENNSYLVANIAN (NORTH AMERICA)

CARBONIFEROUS — 320

MISSISSIPPIAN (NORTH AMERICA)

SEED FERNS

CLUBMOSSES

FERNS

— 360

PROGYMNOSPERMS

ZOSTEROPHYLLS

CLADOXYLALES

DEVONIAN — 408

COOKSONIA AND RHYNIOPHYTES

SILURIAN — 438

ORDOVICIAN — 505

CAMBRIAN — 550

PRECAMBRIAN TIME

58

Index

Acknowledgments

Research, advice, and assistance
Madeline Harley for advice and editorial help on fossil pollen 16–21; Marie Kurmann for advice and editorial help on fossil spores and on gymnosperm pollen 16–19; Darrin Dooling for assistance with photography of living *Equisetum giganteum* 16, *Pronephrium asperum* 17, and cycad cones 19; Alan Hemsley for advice and editorial help on plants 16–21 and plant time chart 58; Pat Herendeen, Else Marie Friis, and Joseph R. Thomasson for editorial help on flowering plants 20–21; Sue Rigby for advice and editorial help on graptolites 22; Douglas Palmer for advice and editorial help on graptolites and corals 22–23 and animal time chart 56–57; Jenny Clack for advice and editorial help on amphibians 32–33, for research on model of *Acanthostega gunnari* 33, and for help, with Elizabeth Hide, on animal time chart 56–57; Michael Coates for advice on classification and for research on *Acanthostega* model 33; Richard Hammond for artwork reference and advice on *Euparkeria capensis* 38–39; and Colin Harrison for advice on birds 44–45.

Makers or owners of models shown in this book
Roby Braun: *Carnotaurus sastrei* 1, 40–41; John Holmes: *Hyracotherium* 5, 49, *Westlothiana lizziae* 3, 34, and *Euoplocephalus tutus* 42–43; Richard Hammond and University Museum, Oxford: *Acanthostega gunnari* 33; Royal Scottish Museum: *Aglaophyton* 16; Natural History Museum, London: *Cothurnocystis eliziae* 26, *Archaeopteryx* 44, and *Smilodon* 48; and Royal British Columbia Museum, Victoria, Canada: woolly mammoth 52–53.

 Model of starfish, p. 27, by Somso-Modelle, Coburg, Germany.

Picture agencies and individuals who have provided photographs for this book
(Abbreviations: t top, b bottom, l left, r right, c centre, a above)
Department of Library Services, American Museum of Natural History/D. Finnin/C. Chesek (negative no. 4956/3) 54bl; Cleveland Museum of Natural History 29br; Simon Conway Morris 22tl; Else Marie Friis 20tr, cr, bl, 21bc; David George 23tr; Pat Herendeen 20bla, bc, br, 21cl, bl; Andrew H. Knoll 8tr, 9bc,br; Ligabue Studies and Research Centre Archive, Venice 42bl; Natural History Museum, London 44bl, 46–47b, 48b; OSF/G. I Bernard 28tl; Douglas Palmer 22br; Sue Rigby 22bl, 22bc; Royal Botanic Gardens, Kew 16cr, 17cla, cl, clb, 18br, bc,

19bl, bc, 21c; Science Photo Library/ Walter Alvarez 6bl, Jeremy Burgess 20tl; Thomas N. Taylor 17tl; and Joseph R. Thomasson 21tl.

Museums that have kindly given permission for Dorling Kindersley to take photographs
University Museum, Oxford; Hunterian Museum, Glasgow University; Natural History Museum, London; Royal Scottish Museum, Edinburgh; Yorkshire Museum; Queensland Museum, South Brisbane; Royal British Columbia Museum, Victoria; Royal Tyrrell Museum of Paleontology, Alberta; Naturmuseum Senckenberg, Frankfurt; and Institut und Museum für Geologie und Paläontologie der Universität Tübingen; *Acanthostega gunnari* skull on p. 33 was photographed at the Zoology Museum, Cambridge while on loan from the Geological Museum, Copenhagen.

Dorling Kindersley photographers
Andy Crawford, Steve Gorton, and Sarah Ashun.

Additional illustrators
Selwyn Hutchinson, Alison Ellis, Mei Lim, Alex Pang, and Ingegerd Svensson (principal illustrators are credited separately on p. 4).